KINGFISHER

FIELD GUIDE

— TO THE —

ROCKS &
MINERALS

OF·THE·WORLD

Key to coloured tabs

The rocks and minerals in this book are arranged into the groups listed below. Minerals are traditionally grouped on the basis of their chemical composition, distinguishing, for example, native elements from oxides or silicates. The rocks are arranged into three groups, as igneous, metamorphic or sedimentary. Use the colour tab on the corner of the pages to find a particular group as you flick through the book.

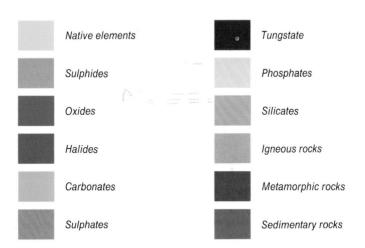

Native elements

Tungstate

Sulphides

Phosphates

Oxides

Silicates

Halides

Igneous rocks

Carbonates

Metamorphic rocks

Sulphates

Sedimentary rocks

KINGFISHER

FIELD GUIDE

—— TO THE ——

ROCKS & MINERALS

OF·THE·WORLD

DAVID COOK & WENDY KIRK

Kingfisher Books

Kingfisher Books, Grisewood & Dempsey Ltd,
Elsley House, 24–30 Great Titchfield Street,
London W1P 7AD

First published in 1991 by Kingfisher Books
Reprinted 1994

BRITISH LIBRARY CATALOGUING IN PUBLICATION DATA
Cook, David
   Kingfisher field guide to the rocks and
minerals of the world.
   I. Title   II. Kirk, Wendy
   552

ISBN 0-06272-1511

Senior Editor: Stuart Cooper
Editors: Keith Lye, Andrea Moran
Cover design: Smiljka Surla

Phototypeset by Southern Positives and Negatives
(SPAN), Lingfield, Surrey
Colour separations by Fotolito Aldini, Milan
Printed in Portugal

CONTENTS

INTRODUCTION

Since the earliest times, people have been fascinated by rocks and minerals. Part of the attraction lies in their economic importance. Indeed the terms Stone Age, Bronze Age and Iron Age indicate periods of history when the uses of these materials were discovered and exploited. Since the onset of the Iron Age, materials from the Earth's crust have been used in myriad ways. Stones, bricks, sand and cement are used in buildings and roads, and iron and steel in engineering. Aviation, ceramics, electronics and metal coating are among the many modern industries that utilize the Earth's mineral resources.

Apart from their uses, many rocks and minerals are attractive in appearance and are sought by eager collectors. The worth of many specimens, including precious stones and metals, is enhanced by special features, such as hardness, brilliance, durability or scarcity. For example, its rarity, appearance and resistance to discolouration gives gold a unique place in international commerce. Other materials, throughout history, have had magical or curative properties ascribed to them.

Minerals and rocks have long given pleasure to many people, both professionals and amateurs. Their study has also enabled us to locate important resources such as oil, and has led to improved techniques for extracting many materials. Several aspects of these sciences, such as crystallography and the dating of rocks, have been established for some time. On the other hand we are gaining new insights into processes that operate inside the Earth. The revolutionary theory of plate tectonics was established only in the 1960s and is still developing. By studying such processes, scientists are able to unravel further the fascinating story of the history of the Earth.

Geological Time Scale		
Era	Period	Time (millions of years ago)
Cenozoic	Quaternary	
		2
	Tertiary	
		65
Mesozoic	Cretaceous	
		145
	Jurassic	
		208
	Triassic	
		245
Paleozoic	Permian	
		290
	Carboniferous	
		362
	Devonian	
		408
	Silurian	
		439
	Ordovician	
		510
	Cambrian	
		570
Precambrian		

HOW TO USE THIS BOOK

The introduction to this book gives a general overview of the subject of rocks and minerals, dealing with their formation, occurrence and the qualities to note when making an identification. Many of the technical terms used by geologists to describe minerals and rocks are also explained, including definitions of the headings found in the fact panel. Further definitions can be found in the Glossary on pages 31–33. Because of the technical nature of the subject, it is worth familiarizing yourself with these concepts before consulting the individual entries.

Each page is devoted to a different species, and contains some explanatory text, with photographs of examples of different forms of the rock or mineral concerned. In the case of some minerals, line drawings illustrate the crystal structure or cleavage patterns. A fact panel summarizes the main features, against which you can check any specimen you have found. The most important identifying features of minerals are asterisked.

The colour shows which group of rocks or minerals each entry belongs to, for quick reference. The colour code is explained on page 2.

Typical examples are illustrated with photographs. Line drawings in some entries illustrate specific features such as crystal form.

A text summarizes the main features of a rock or mineral and describes any notable varieties. Information is given about uses, famous localities and the origin of names.

Labels point out important features for identification.

A fact panel includes detailed information about the properties of the species. Asterisks denote the most important distinguishing features of minerals. Examples are provided of large deposits or particularly fine specimens.

Kyanite Al₂SiO₅

Kyanite is also known as disthene, meaning 'double strength'. This refers to the fact that the hardness along the length of kyanite crystals is less than the hardness across them. This is the mineral's most characteristic feature. Kyanite is mined in several parts of the world for use as a refractory material. Transparent crystals are occasionally used in jewellery. The most valued colours are deep cornflower-blue, pale azure-blue and bluish-green. Like the other aluminium silicate polymorphs, kyanite is an indicator of metamorphic conditions. It is formed at moderate temperatures and at moderate to high pressures in pelitic rocks, and is often associated with garnet, staurolite and corundum. The name is derived from the Greek word *kyanos*, meaning 'a dark blue substance'.

Bladed crystals

Kyanite

Kyanite

kyanite porphyroblasts

KYANITE

*Colour	blue, sometimes white or colourless at margins
Lustre	vitreous, pearly on cleavage surfaces
Transparency	transparent to subtranslucent
Streak	white
*Hardness	5–7 varying with direction
*Cleavage	two good cleavages
Fracture	brittle
*Habit	as flat bladed crystals in schists and gneisses, and as radiating rosettes in quartz
Specific gravity	3.5–3.7
Twinning	frequent
Crystal system	triclinic
Alteration	to a shimmer aggregate of white mica and quartz
Occurrence	in regionally metamorphosed rocks, i.e. schists, gneisses, eclogites and amphibolites; may be associated with garnet or staurolite, also in associated pegmatites and quartz veins, a central mineral
Examples	good blue crystals at Pizzo Forno, Candon Ticino (Switzerland); enormous crystals at Minas Gerais (Brazil); green crystals up to 30 cm (12 in) long at Machakos (Kenya); large deposits at Chesterfield, Massachusetts, Litchfield, Connecticut and Yancey County, North Carolina (USA); also India, Kenya and Australia

94

Introduction

THE EARTH: A CHEMICAL MACHINE

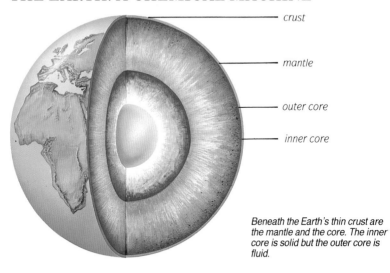

crust

mantle

outer core

inner core

Beneath the Earth's thin crust are the mantle and the core. The inner core is solid but the outer core is fluid.

In order to study rocks and minerals it is useful to know something of the Earth's composition and formation. The Earth as a whole has a particular chemical constitution but within it are a wide range of rocks and minerals of diverse chemical make-up. Minerals may be scarce, occurring as small grains, or may occur in high concentrations, sometimes of economic importance. Rocks vary from dull, soft clays to hard, bright, crystalline granites. What then are the forces that have formed the Earth and its major chemical components?

The Earth consists of an extremely dense core, a fairly dense mantle and a relatively thin light crust. The core itself consists of a liquid outer layer and a solid inner layer. Gravity, a major force that shapes the Earth, has concentrated heavy materials such as iron and its sulphides into the core, while light magnesium and aluminium silicates dominate in the crust.

oceanic ridg

upper mantle

subduction zone

molten rock ri

Introduction

Heat is important in shaping the Earth. Heat creates the large-scale convection currents in the mantle which help to move large slabs of crust and upper mantle, known as *plates*, around the surface of the Earth. New plate material is produced at *constructive plate margins*, usually ocean ridges. The plates move apart at a rate of 2–18cm (0.8–7.2in) per year. This is balanced, however, by the loss of material at *destructive plate margins*. Here plates move into the mantle down *subduction zones* where they melt to form magma.

Most of our knowledge of rocks and minerals is of those in the Earth's crust; relatively little is known about the composition of the mantle and core. But it is thought that the upper mantle may contain such heavy rocks as peridotite, which appears occasionally on the surface, but is heavier than most crustal rocks. This guide describes many of the rocks and minerals in the crust and the processes that formed them.

What are minerals and rocks?

First, we can define the terms rocks and minerals. Minerals are naturally occurring, *inorganic* (lifeless) substances. Coal, oil and natural gas are not minerals, because they are mixtures of organic chemicals formed from once-living matter. They are usually called fossil fuels. Minerals consist of elements, substances that cannot be broken down into other substances by chemical means. Some minerals, called the *native elements* consist of only one element, for example platinum or gold. However, most are chemical combinations of two or more elements (see page 18). Each mineral has a definite composition and any part of a mineral is much the same as any other part. Rocks are composed of mineral grains, but the proportions of minerals vary from one sample to another. Sometimes, as in limestone, a rock is composed mostly of one mineral, but most rocks consist of a number of different minerals.

The diagram shows oceanic crust being produced at an ocean ridge. New rock is formed from magma rising from the mantle. It is carried from the ridge on a moving plate of upper mantle. The plate is then forced downwards beneath a plate margin of continental crust. Rocks on the descending plate melt. The molten material rises and forms intrusions and volcanoes.

new mountain chain

volcanic islands

oceanic crust

continental plate

convection currents

Introduction

MINERALS

Minerals are the building blocks that make up rocks. Scientists describe minerals as naturally occurring, inorganic substances. Nearly all minerals have a definite atomic structure that gives them a characteristic crystal shape. The study of minerals is the oldest branch of Earth science. For example, the recognition and use of copper probably dates back to 6000 BC. Collecting minerals has become a very popular hobby, and this field guide describes the properties used to identify minerals. This is often not easy, and requires careful observation using a hand lens, and lots of practice. A few simple chemical tests are given, but great care must be taken when using these. The most useful features for identifying each mineral are given an asterisk (*) in the main text.

Colour

This is the most familiar property of minerals, but is often not the most useful, because many minerals show a variety of colours depending on the impurities they contain. For example, quartz may be colourless, white, pink, yellow, mauve, blue or black. Some minerals nearly always have the same colour due to their chemical composition. Here, colour can be useful in identification. For example, sulphur is bright yellow, malachite is always green, azurite is always blue. These minerals are said to be *idiochromatic*, as opposed to minerals of variable colour, which are said to be *allochromatic*.

Streak

More consistent and reliable than a mineral's colour is the colour of its streak (the mineral in powdered form). The streak is consistent regardless of colour variation in different specimens. It is usually produced by scratching the mineral across a piece of unglazed porcelain, or by crushing a small portion. A penknife may also be used to scratch the surface and produce a powder. Idiochromatic minerals usually have a streak which is slightly lighter than the colour of the specimen. Allochromatic minerals generally have a white or greyish white streak. However, some minerals show a streak which contrasts with the colour of the mineral. For example, the pale gold mineral pyrite has a yellowish black streak, while grey-black hematite produces a cherry-red one. Streak is rarely a diagnostic property of the silicate minerals. These are often too hard to produce a streak, and it is usually white.

Streak, the colour of a mineral in powder form, is a guide to the identification of some minerals, because it differs from their normal colour. Hematite, an iron mineral, is grey to black. But if you scrape the surface the streak will be dark red to reddish brown.

Introduction

Lustre

This refers to the amount and quality of reflected light coming from the surface of the mineral. It may be *metallic* or *non-metallic*. A metallic lustre is produced by opaque minerals that absorb a lot of light. This is the lustre of metals and is also shown by many sulphides, such as chalcopyrite. A less perfect metallic lustre, known as *sub-metallic*, is shown by some of the semi-opaque oxides, such as hematite. A non-metallic lustre is shown by transparent and translucent minerals. It includes a variety of types, as defined below:

Adamantine a high degree of sparkle, as shown by diamond.

Vitreous the lustre of broken glass, as in quartz and many of the silicates. (Calcite shows a sub-vitreous lustre.)

Resinous the lustre of resin, as in amber, opal and some varieties of sphalerite.

Pearly the lustre of a pearl, caused by the reflection of light from a series of parallel surfaces within a crystal. It is shown by talc and cleavage faces of selenite (gypsum).

Silky the lustre of silk. This is confined to minerals that have a fibrous structure, such as satin spar, a variety of gypsum.

Greasy this is produced in minerals with tiny irregularities on the surface, such as nepheline.

Earthy minerals that do not show a lustre are said to be earthy or dull.

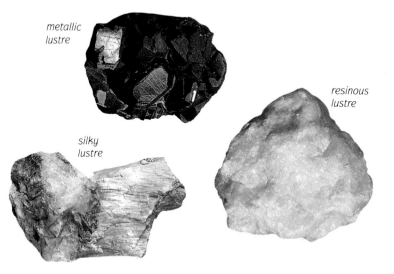

metallic lustre

resinous lustre

silky lustre

Transparency

Mineralogists usually indicate the transparency of minerals – that is, whether the mineral is *transparent*, *translucent*, or *opaque*. But these terms are rarely of value in mineral identification. The degree of transparency depends to a large extent on how thick the specimen is, and also on the presence of inclusions (fragments of other substances within the specimen), cleavage planes and any internal flaws.

Introduction

Hardness
Hardness is a measure of the resistance of a mineral to scratching or abrasion. It is given as a number between 1 and 10 according to a reference set of minerals set up by the Austrian mineralogist Friedrich Mohs in 1812. Number 1 is the softest and number 10 is the hardest. Each mineral can scratch any with a lower number, but can be scratched only by those with a higher number.

The hardness of a mineral is determined by finding which minerals in Mohs' scale scratch it, and which it will scratch. It is best to use a hand lens, as a softer mineral may leave a powder trail when scraped along a harder mineral, giving the false impression of a scratch. Where these minerals are not available, the test can be carried out using a fingernail (hardness 2–2.5), a copper coin (hardness 3) or a steel knife-blade (hardness 5.5–6.5). Minerals with a hardness over 6 will scratch glass.

MOHS' SCALE

1. Talc   2. Gypsum   3. Calcite   4. Fluorite

5. Apatite   6. Orthoclase   7. Quartz

8. Topaz   9. Corundum   10. Diamond

Cleavage
Many minerals tend to break along sets of well-defined planes, which are related to the internal arrangement of the atoms. This property is known as *cleavage*, and a mineral may break in one or more directions. For example, mica shows a good cleavage in one direction, readily splitting into thin sheets. This is because the bonding between atoms within the sheets is much stronger than the bonding between the sheets. This type of cleavage is known as *basal cleavage*. Cleavage is related to the crystal system to which a mineral belongs (see the section on 'Crystal systems' below). Galena, which crystallizes in the cubic system, shows an excellent cleavage in three directions parallel to the faces of a cube. Fluorite, which also crystallizes in the cubic system, shows octahedral cleavage – that is the cleavage is parallel to the faces of an octahedron. Other directions commonly encountered are parallel to prism faces, pyramid faces, or the faces of a rhombohedron. Some specimens may show surfaces known as *partings*, which are superficially similar to, but more widely spaced than cleavage planes. They are different in origin from cleavage and are not present in all specimens of any one mineral.

rhombohedral cleavage

basal cleavage

conchoidal fracture

Fracture

This term refers to the shape of the broken surface of the mineral, as opposed to the cleavage surface and is occasionally of use in identification. Terms used to describe fracture are as follows:

Conchoidal fracture is the most distinctive, and is that shown by broken glass. The mineral breaks with a concave or convex surface, which often shows concentric ridges looking rather like growth lines on a shell. It is shown by quartz and olivine.

Even the fracture surface is flattish, as in garnet.

Uneven most minerals show this kind of fracture, where the surface is characterized by minute elevations and depressions.

Hackly the fracture surface is covered with small, jagged points, as in native copper.

Tenacity

This property is included with fracture in this guide. Tenacity refers to the way minerals react to shock, crushing, cutting and bending. Terms used are as follows:

Sectile the mineral can be cut with a knife, and the slice breaks up under a hammer, as in graphite.

Malleable a slice from the mineral will flatten when hammered, as in native copper.

Flexible thin sheets of the mineral will bend, as in talc.

Elastic the bent portion will spring back when pressure is released. For example, mica flakes are flexible and elastic, whereas talc and molybdenite are flexible but inelastic.

Brittle most minerals are brittle, and will crumble when hit, as in iron pyrites and fluorspar.

Introduction

Specific gravity
Although rarely determined accurately, specific gravity may be a useful property whenever a specimen feels lighter or heavier than 'normal'. Specific gravity is the ratio of the weight of a body to that of an equal volume of water. Most minerals and rocks show a specific gravity of between 2.5 and 3. With practice, the specific gravity of an unknown mineral can be estimated; where this departs from the normal range, it is usually on the high side. The relationship between colour and specific gravity may be helpful, because dark minerals are often relatively heavy, whereas light coloured minerals are often relatively light. Exceptions to this rule can therefore be identified fairly easily. For example, baryte, a white mineral, appears surprisingly heavy (specific gravity = 4.5), whereas dark grey graphite feels light (specific gravity = 2.23). Examples of other minerals with a high specific gravity are the ore minerals galena (7.5), pyrite (5.0) and chalcopyrite (4.2).

Alteration
After a mineral is formed, various conditions may cause it to change or alter to other minerals. Common alteration processes are weathering and hydrothermal activity. Alteration products can be a good clue to the identity of the original mineral, especially those that have characteristic colours.

Other features
Some minerals have unusual properties that may be useful in identification. Some of these characteristics are given below:

Magnetism magnetite is the only common mineral which is strongly magnetic. This property distinguishes it from chromite.
Taste halite (rock salt) and sylvite can be distinguished by their taste. Sylvite tastes like rock salt, but is more bitter.
Odour a few minerals can be identified by their smell when hit, rubbed or heated. For example, when pyrite is struck it gives off a smell of burning sulphur. When arsenic compounds are heated, they give off a smell of garlic.
Fluorescence some minerals glow in the dark when exposed to ultraviolet light or X-rays. This is known as *fluorescence*, after the mineral fluorite, which illustrates this property well.
Phosphorescence minerals which glow in the dark for a time after being exposed to light are called *phosphorescent*.
Piezoelectricity and pyroelectricity when some minerals are stressed, they acquire an electric charge. This is described as a *piezoelectric effect*. Quartz, which has this property, is frequently used in electrical equipment and in radio receivers and transmitters. Other minerals become charged when heated. It has long been known that tourmaline, when heated in the embers of a fire, first attracts and then repels the ashes. This is known as *pyroelectricity*.
Radioactivity certain elements are *radioactive*, emitting radiation which can be detected using a Geiger counter. This property is shown by pitchblende, which is the main ore of uranium.

Introduction

Crystals

Most minerals, if allowed to grow unrestricted, will form crystals. Crystals are more or less symmetrical solids bounded by flat (or *planar*) faces. The crystal shape reflects the internal arrangement of the atoms, which pack together in a regular three-dimensional framework. The best crystals are formed by slow, uninterrupted growth. Some minerals readily form large, well shaped crystals, whereas others do so only rarely. The study of crystals may be useful in identifying certain minerals, such as garnet and pyrites, as they form particular shapes.

Habit and form

The set of faces produced by the symmetry of the crystal is known as the *form*. Crystals of the same mineral may look very different, as a single mineral may show more than one form. For example, pyrite has both cubic and octahedral crystals.

If the form totally encloses a space, as in a cube, it is said to be *closed*. If not, it is said to be *open*. An example of this is a prism, which is not closed at the ends. Open forms must always be combined with other forms.

The form commonly taken by single crystals is described in this guide under the heading 'Habit'. Some minerals do not form crystals at all, but are *amorphous*, forming structureless masses.

botryoidal
habit

acicular habit

Habit refers to the appearance of single crystals or crystalline *aggregates* that do not show perfect crystal shapes. In a crystal, some faces may grow better than others. For example, a mineral may show well developed prism faces, so that it is much longer in one direction than the other two. Its habit is then described as *prismatic*. Other terms are:

Acicular fine, needle-shaped crystals, as in rutile.
Bladed flattened like a knife-blade, as in kyanite.
Botryoidal like a bunch of grapes, as in chalcedony.
Dendritic branching tree-like or moss-like, as in native copper.
Fibrous fine, thread-like strands, as in asbestos.
Mammilated round and mutually interfering masses, as in malachite; the protuberances are larger and more flattened than botryoidal.
Massive crystalline aggregates with no regular form.
Radiating radial crystals or fibres, as in nodular pyrite.
Reniform kidney-shaped, as in hematite.
Tabular showing broad, flat surfaces, as in baryte.

Introduction

Crystal systems

Crystals may be grouped together into seven systems based on their symmetry. Crystals may show one or more planes and/or axes of symmetry, and may have a centre of symmetry. A plane of symmetry can be illustrated using a matchbox. There are three ways in which this can be cut into two parts, so that one half is the mirror image of the other. Thus it shows three planes of symmetry.

The matchbox also shows three lines or axes of symmetry, each passing through the centres of two opposite faces, so that when it is rotated once about each axis, the same view appears twice. Thus the matchbox is said to show three *axes* of *two-fold rotation*. Similarly, crystals may show axes of *three-*, *four-*, or *six-fold rotation*. The matchbox, and many crystals, has a centre of symmetry, as each face on one side has a corresponding parallel face on the other.

Each crystal system is defined by the number and types of symmetry elements present. To each system are assigned reference axes, which determine the orientation of the crystal faces. In most crystal systems, the reference axes lie along the axes of symmetry. The angles between them vary from system to system. The characteristics of each system are summarized in the table opposite. Examples of crystal forms in each system are illustrated.

The regular shapes of the crystals shown here may not be so apparent in real specimens. This is because some crystal faces may grow larger than others, and their shape is altered. However, the angle between any two particular faces is always the same for all crystals of the same mineral.

CRYSTAL SYSTEMS

Crystals that belong to the cubic crystal system must all have 4 three-fold axes of symmetry. There are 3 reference axes, a_1, a_2 and a_3. They are all at right angles to each other and are of equal length.

Crystals of the tetragonal crystal system are characterized by the presence of a single vertical axis of four-fold symmetry. There are 3 reference axes, all at right angles. The vertical axis, c, differs in length from the horizontal axes, a_1 and a_2.

The orthorhombic crystal system is characterized by 3 perpendicular two-fold axes of symmetry, or 1 two-fold axis at the intersection of two perpendicular planes of symmetry. The 3 reference axes, a, b and c, are at right angles to each other, but are of different lengths.

Monoclinic crystals must contain 1 two-fold axis of symmetry. The reference axes, a, b and c, are of different lengths. The vertical axis, c, is not at right angles to axis a. The symmetry axis, b, is at right angles to the plane containing the other two.

Crystals of the triclinic system have either no symmetry or just a centre of symmetry. There are 3 reference axes, a, b, and c, of different lengths, none of which are at right angles to each other.

The hexagonal system has 1 vertical six-fold axis of symmetry, while the trigonal system has a three-fold one. They have the same reference axes. The three horizontal ones, a_1, a_2 and a_3, are equal in length and at an angle of 120° to each other. The vertical axis, c, differs in length to the other three.

Cubic	*modified cube* **Galena**	*icositetrahedron* **Andradite**	*octahedron* **Diamond**
Tetragonal	*pyramidal* **Cassiterite**	**Wulfenite**	**Zircon**
Orthorhombic	**Baryte**	**Olivine**	*pyramidal* **Sulphur**
Monoclinic		**Epidote**	**Gypsum**
Triclinic		**Axinite**	**Rhodonite**
hexagonal and trigonal		*hexagonal prism* **Apatite**	**Quartz**

Introduction

Twinning

A twinned crystal is made up of two or more parts. One part of the crysta
is in a reversed orientation to the adjacent part. Twins are recognized by
the presence of *re-entrant* angles (angles that point inwards).

Twinning can occur simply by contact across a flat surface, forming
contact twins, such as in rutile. In other cases, the twin cannot be divided
into two separate halves, rather the halves appear to have grown through
each other. These are known as *interpenetrant twins*, as seen in fluorite
Twins may be single or repeated (*polysynthetic*), as in albite.

contact twin

interpenetrant twin

Chemistry of minerals

Each mineral has a distinctive chemical composition, which may be
fixed, or may vary within certain limits. This composition is expressed as
a chemical formula. Some minerals, known as the *native elements*
contain only one element. Most minerals, however, are compounds
containing more than one element. They comprise two charged parts
called *ions*. The negatively charged *anions* often contain oxygen. The
symbols for the elements used in this field guide are given below, together
with the names and formulas of common anions referred to.

Symbols for Elements				Common Anionic Groups	
Ag	Silver	Li	Lithium	Al_2O_4	Aluminate
Al	Aluminium	Mg	Magnesium	As	Arsenide
As	Arsenic	Mn	Manganese	AsO_4	Arsenate
Au	Gold	Mo	Molybdenum	BO_3	Borate
B	Boron	Na	Sodium	Cl	Chloride
Ba	Barium	O	Oxygen	CO_3	Carbonate
Be	Beryllium	P	Phosphorus	CrO_4	Chromate
Bi	Bismuth	Pb	Lead	F	Fluoride
C	Carbon	Pt	Platinum	MoO_4	Molybdate
Ca	Calcium	S	Sulphur	N	Nitride
Cl	Chlorine	Sb	Antimony	NO_3	Nitrate
Co	Cobalt	Si	Silicon	O	Oxide
Cr	Chromium	Sn	Tin	OH	Hydroxide
Cu	Copper	Sr	Strontium	PO_4	Phosphate
F	Fluorine	Ti	Titanium	S	Sulphide
Fe	Iron	U	Uranium	SiO_4	Silicate
H	Hydrogen	W	Tungsten	SO_4	Sulphate
Hg	Mercury	Zn	Zinc	TiO_3	Titanate
K	Potassium	Zr	Zirconium	WO_4	Tungstate

Introduction

An example of a simple mineral formula is NaCl, the formula for halite, or sodium chloride. It contains one sodium atom and one chlorine atom per molecule. A slightly more complicated formula is that for calcite, $CaCO_3$, or rutile, TiO_2. The numbers refer to the number of atoms of the preceding element that are present in one molecule of the mineral. Sometimes minerals form chemical series. An example of this is the olivine series, written as $(Mg,Fe)SiO_4$. This means that atoms of magnesium and iron can substitute for one another, to form a continuously variable series from a pure magnesium olivine to a pure iron olivine.

Chemical tests
Some simple chemical tests are helpful in identifying minerals. In particular, geologists carry dilute hydrochloric acid (HCl) in the field. If a drop is placed on calcite, it will effervesce (fizz, giving off gas), whereas quartz does not react. This is one way in which the two superficially similar minerals can be distinguished. Dolomite, another carbonate mineral like calcite, also reacts, but the reaction is much slower. Great care must be taken even when using dilute acids to avoid contact with skin and clothes, and to avoid breathing in fumes.

Where laboratory facilities are available, other chemical tests can be carried out, such as for solubility in acids. A powdered sample of the mineral is placed in acid in a test-tube and, if required, is gently warmed. Flame colouration tests are carried out by holding a chip of mineral in a flame with a pair of forceps. The hottest part of the flame is used, at the tip of the blue cone. The colour of the flame indicates which element is present. For example, a green flame indicates baryte, which contains barium.

Field occurrence of minerals

All rocks are made up of minerals, but good mineral specimens are not common. Crystals grow unobstructed only in cavities, joints and fissures. Just a few minerals make up most of the volume of rocks in the Earth's crust. These are called *rock-forming minerals*, most of which are silicates. The main ones are quartz, alkali and plagioclase feldspars, muscovite and biotite micas, pyroxenes (especially augite), amphiboles (especially hornblende) and olivine. Calcite (calcium carbonate) is an important rock-forming mineral in sedimentary rocks, as is dolomite.

Mineral deposits are unusual concentrations of minerals that have formed by special processes, and may be present at sufficiently high levels to warrant extracting. There are several ways in which they are formed.

When magma cools to form igneous rocks, minerals may become concentrated in particular areas. Economic deposits of native elements, such as platinum, have been found in this setting, as have some oxides, such as magnetite, and sulphides such as pyrite and chalcopyrite.

Pegmatites often contain large crystals of minerals that would normally occur only in minute amounts. Pegmatites are formed during the last stages of crystallization of the magma, when the liquid is rich in water and many uncommon elements. Pegmatites commonly form veins and dykes around or within granite masses. Economic deposits of quartz,

Introduction

feldspar and mica form in this way. Pegmatites also yield such gemstones as beryl, garnet, topaz and tourmaline.

During the late stages of cooling of a magma, heated gases containing volatile elements such as boron, chlorine and fluorine stream out into the adjacent country rock. Minerals containing these elements will eventually crystallize as *pneumatolitic ore deposits*. These are common around granite intrusions, and may include tourmaline, topaz and fluorite.

During the final stages of cooling, hot fluids called *hydrothermal solutions* may react with the host rock to form replacement deposits, or precipitate into cracks and fissures to form veins. These may contain economically important minerals known as *ore*, together with minerals of no commercial value, known as *gangue*.

When mineral veins are exposed to weathering, they may be drastically altered. Secondary deposits are formed by the reaction of minerals at the surface with air and water. Solutions that leach down from the vein may react with primary ores, forming a zone of oxidized ores above the water table, and a zone of *secondary (supergene) sulphide enrichment* below it.

Sometimes the host rock may react with hot fluids to produce new minerals, a process called *metasomatism*. The term *skarn* is used for limestones that have been altered to form a variety of minerals, including epidote, olivine, vesuvianite, and ugrandite garnets, together with some ore minerals and boron-bearing minerals such as tourmaline.

The weathering of sedimentary rocks by wind and water may alter their composition, removing some components and concentrating others. These deposits may contain original minerals that are less prone to weathering, such as tin, gold, baryte and kyanite, or entirely new ones. An example of the latter type is bauxite, an important ore of aluminium.

Detrital deposits are sediments formed by the breakdown of existing rocks. In *placer deposits*, minerals that existed in only small amounts in the parent rock may become concentrated. In *alluvial deposits* (carried by a river), minerals are separated out according to density, and chemically resistant minerals, such as gold, cassiterite, ruby and garnet, may form important deposits.

Mineral deposits are also precipitated due to the evaporation of sea water. Halite and anhydrite are formed in this way. Evaporites can also form in desert areas, such as where transitory lakes dry out.

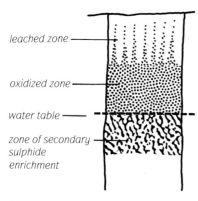

leached zone

oxidized zone

water table

zone of secondary sulphide enrichment

Left: Where a mineral vein has been altered at the surface by weathering, water may leach out and transport salts downwards. Chemical reactions take place between descending solutions and existing minerals, to produce an economic deposit of ore.

Right: Transparent varieties of beryl are popular as gemstones. The photograph shows green emerald, pale blue aquamarine, yellow heliodor, pink morganite and colourless goshenite. To show off their best qualities the gems are cut and polished, the many facets reflecting light back out of the crystal. The pale heliodor at the left shows the oblong emerald cut typically used for beryl.

Introduction

Gemstones

Gemstones have long been prized for their beautiful colours, attractive lustres and crystal forms. These minerals were thought to have special properties, some of which brought luck to the wearer, while others were thought to be capable of warding off or curing diseases. The mineral nephrite (a variety of jade) is named from the Greek *nephros*, meaning 'kidney', due to its alleged powers in protecting the wearer against kidney complaints. Findings in prehistoric caves in Europe have shown that gold and amber have been used for jewellery for several thousand years. Serpentine and obsidian have probably been used for much longer.

The beauty of a mineral may depend on its colour, transparency or lustre. Red rubies and green emeralds are attractively coloured, transparent and brilliant, whereas diamonds owe their popularity to their lustre and fire (the way they disperse light). The beauty of turquoise is in its azure-blue colour.

Rarity is an important factor in determining the value of a gem, as is durability. A gem should be able to resist physical and chemical damage. Softer gemstones, such as opal and peridot (olivine), are likely to lose their brilliance and colour in time and are unsuitable for setting in rings.

Many gemstones have become famous in their own right. For example, the largest diamond ever found was the Cullinan. This diamond measures about 12.5 cm (5 in) across, and was found at Premier Mine (South Africa) in 1905. It weighed 3106 metric carats (more than 1.3 lbs). It was cut into 105 gemstones, the largest of which weighs 516 carats and is known as the Star of Africa. It is set in the British Royal Sceptre.

Other famous diamonds include the Indian *Koh-i-noor* (Persian for 'Mountain of Light'), which was presented to Queen Victoria in 1850. The history of this diamond has been traced back to 1304. It has changed hands several times as a result of war and conquest.

Introduction

This section through a volcanic region shows the formation of igneous rocks. Magma rises from a large underground chamber (1), up the volcano's central vent (2) or through a side vent (3). During eruptions, ash (4), which conists of tiny fragments of magma, may be shot into the air and lava (5) flows out of the vent. Many volcanoes are composed of alternating layers of ash and lava (6). Lava can also reach the surface through fissures (7), where it spreads out without building a volcano. Magma which hardens on the surface forms extrusive igneous rocks. Some magma hardens underground to create intrusive igneous rocks. Steeply inclined sheets of magma form dykes (8). Sills (9) are

ROCKS

With few exceptions, geologists classify rocks in three groups according to the way they were formed. These groups are *igneous*, *metamorphic* or *sedimentary* rocks.

Igneous rocks

Igneous rocks, such as basalts and granites, are those produced from hot magma rising up from the lower crust or upper mantle, which then cools and solidifies. *Extrusive* igneous rocks form from magma that is ejected from the crust (as in volcanoes) and cools on the surface, while *intrusive* rocks form from magma solidifying underground. Intrusive rocks may eventually be exposed at the surface, however, if the rock above them is weathered away.

Two main factors affect the nature of igneous rocks – the cooling rate of the magma and its chemical constitution. When magma reaches the Earth's surface as lava and flows either onto land or into the oceans, or is violently ejected, cooling is very rapid. This results either in *fine-grained* rocks, such as basalt, which are made up of tiny crystals, or *glassy* rocks, such as obsidian, where there has not been enough time for crystals to grow. On the other hand, when magmas are emplaced in the Earth's crust as *igneous intrusions*, they cool slowly and crystals have more time to grow. In very large intrusions, cooling is extremely slow, and *coarse-grained* rocks are formed, such as granites and gabbros. Smaller intrusions are characterized by *medium-grained* rocks, such as dolerite.

Plutons are large intrusions, often of granite, that extend deep down into the crust. Intrusions called *batholiths* cover up to hundreds of parallel to existing beds. Bodies called laccoliths (10) push up the overlying rocks into domes. The largest masses of magma are batholiths (not shown here). Steep-sided volcanoes such as this, which produce a lot of ash, are formed from acid to intermediate magma. Most dykes and sills, however, are produced by the more fluid basic lavas.

thousands of square kilometres in area. Smaller bodies (up to tens of square kilometres) are called *stocks*. *Dykes* and *sills* are sheet-like bodies of igneous rock which vary in size from centimetres to hundreds of metres wide. Dykes are vertical or near-vertical, cutting across bedding planes of sedimentary rocks, while sills usually follow them and are essentially horizontal. *Veins* are small irregular networks.

Volcanic rocks also occur in different forms. Basic lavas are of low viscosity and can flow from fissures over large areas. These are called *plateau lavas*. Rapid cooling under water gives rise to *pillow lavas* named after their characteristic shape. When lava and fragments (*pyroclasts*) are ejected from pipe-like vents, they form volcanic cones.

The formation of the oceanic crust is a mixture of extrusive and intrusive processes. This particular type of igneous rock is important, because vast quantities are produced at the ocean ridges. *Ophiolites* are exposed pieces of oceanic crust that are pushed above sea level.

Texture

The most important textural feature of an igneous rock is its grain size. The crystals in fine-grained rocks cannot be distinguished with the naked eye, because they measure less than 0.1mm (0.004in) across. Medium-grained rocks contain crystals that may be distinguished by eye, between about 0.1mm and 2mm (0.004–0.08in), while coarse-grained rocks have grains that are larger than 2mm (0.08in).

Often the magma is not completely molten, but contains crystals of minerals that have a high melting point. On cooling, these large crystals are surrounded by finer-grained material known as the *matrix*. They are especially noticeable in the finer-grained rocks. Such *phenocrysts* may be included in the name of the rock, as in olivine basalt.

Introduction

Structure
The structure of a rock refers to features that are on a larger scale than the textural relationship between the component grains:

Layered or **banded structure** is made apparent by differently coloured or textured bands.

Vesicular structure is caused when bubbles of gas escape from a magma leaving cavities (*vesicles*) in the rock. If these vesicles are filled with secondary minerals they are called *amygdales*.

Xenoliths are pieces of other rock embedded in an igneous rock. They are usually fragments of host rock which fall into the magma.

amygdaloidal structure

vesicular structure

Colour
Rocks containing mainly light-coloured or *felsic* minerals are termed *leucocratic*. With increasing content of dark-coloured or *mafic* minerals, the rock becomes *melanocratic*. If dark minerals make up more than 90 per cent, the rock is called *ultramafic*. Most coloured minerals are magnesium- and iron-bearing (*ferromagnesian*), and include olivines and pyroxenes. The colour comes from the iron. The *colour index* is the percentage of dark-coloured minerals in a rock. It is usually estimated and can be seen only in coarse- to medium-grained rocks.

Mineralogy
The minerals encountered most frequently in igneous rocks act as a means of classification. Referred to as *essential minerals*, they come from a relatively small group of rock-forming silicates. These are the light coloured minerals quartz, the feldspars and feldspathoids and the dark coloured pyroxenes, olivines, micas and amphiboles. Most rocks contain relatively few, perhaps two to four, essential minerals. Minerals occurring in minor amounts in the rock are called *accessory minerals*. Rocks with a colour index of less than 90 per cent are classified using the QAPF diagram shown on page 25. The diagram consists of two triangles, QAP and APF, where Q=quartz, A=alkali feldspar, P=plagioclase and F=feldspathoid. A rock can be plotted on the diagram, and named according to the relative proportions of its felsic minerals.

Rocks are also classified chemically by the quantity of silica (SiO_2) they contain. This may be chemically combined, as in the silicate minerals, or if sufficient silica is present it forms free quartz. The rock is then said to be *oversaturated*. Rocks may be classed as *acid*, *intermediate*, *basic* or *ultrabasic*, as the content of silica decreases.

Introduction

QAPF DIAGRAM

1. Quartzolite and quartz-rich granitoids
2. Alkali feldspar granite
3. Granite
4. Granodiorite
5. Tonalite
6. Alkali feldspar syenite
7. Syenite
8. Monzonite
9. Monzodiorite and monzogabbro
10. Diorite, gabbro and anorthosite
11. Feldspathoid syenite
12. Feldspathoid monzosyenite
13. Feldspathoid monzodiorite and feldspathoid monzogabbro
14. Feldspathoid diorite and feldspathoid gabbro
15. Foidolite

$Q + A + P = 100$

$A + P + F = 100$

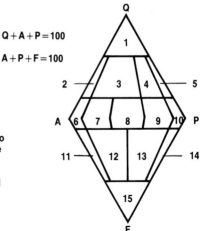

The QAPF diagram is used to classify igneous rocks. The different regions represent rocks of different composition. A rock in which the felsic minerals were 100 per cent quartz would plot at point Q and would therefore be called a quartzolite.

Metamorphic rocks

Metamorphic rocks are produced by the alteration of all types of rocks in the solid state under high temperatures and/or pressures. This involves changes in mineralogy (recrystallization of existing minerals or formation of new ones) and usually changes in texture compared with the original rock type. The major group of metamorphic rocks have undergone *regional metamorphism*, usually during mountain-forming episodes, when the rocks are subjected to elevated pressures and temperatures.

The diagram shows how pressure and heat during mountain building metamorphoses the sedimentary rock shale into slate. Heat from magma transforms limestones into the metamorphic rock marble.

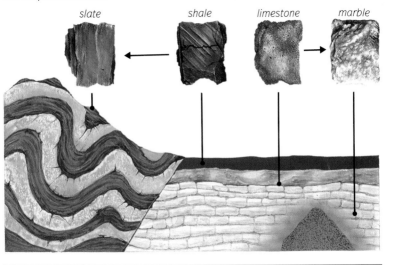

slate   shale   limestone   marble

Introduction

The forces involved in building mountain chains, such as the Alps and Himalayas, cause the rocks to be broken to form *faults* and bent to form *folds*. Areas of several hundred kilometres may be affected. *Dynamic metamorphism* refers to the alteration of rocks under higher pressures but lower temperatures. *Contact*, or *thermal metamorphism* occurs around igneous intrusions where the heat of the intrusion 'bakes' the surrounding country rock to form a *contact metamorphic aureole*. The size of such aureoles depends on such factors as the volume and temperature of the intruded magma. The degree of metamorphism is referred to as the *grade*. It increases from low- to medium- to high-grade with increasing temperatures and pressures. Higher grade rocks have a texture (or fabric) that is more crystalline and less like the original rock, and contain certain minerals (*index minerals*) which form only above specific temperature and pressure conditions.

Texture

Texture is an important aid to identification. Metamorphic rocks vary in grain size, becoming coarser with increasing temperature. Thus *slates* are fine-grained, *schists*, medium-grained and *gneisses* are coarse-grained. If the grains are roughly the same size, the texture is described as *granoblastic*. However, some minerals grow better than others and may form large, well-shaped crystals surrounded by a finer-grained matrix, giving rise to a *porphyroblastic* texture. If these crystals contain inclusions of smaller ones they are called *poikiloblasts*.

The recrystallization of minerals under pressure often causes the grains in the rock to be arranged in layers, known as *foliation*. Slates are characterized by a closely-spaced foliation, whereas *schistose* rocks have roughly parallel layers. Gneisses show a layered structure (*gneissose foliation*), with bands of quartz and feldspar alternating with bands of darker minerals. Hornfels is a hard rock produced by contact metamorphism that usually has no directional alignment of crystals.

Structure

Original sedimentary and igneous structures (or *relict* structures) may be preserved. *Bedding* (layering) is the most obvious sedimentary structure. Features such as fossils and graded bedding, which can be used to find the original top of the bed, may also be preserved. Such structures are better preserved in low-grade rocks.

schistosity

folding

Introduction

The main metamorphic features are *cleavage* and *folding*. Cleavage allows such rocks as slates and phyllites to split into sheets along parallel planes of foliation developed during metamorphism. There is no relationship between the original bedding and the imposed cleavage, so *cleavage planes* are usually at an angle to bedding. Most regionally metamorphosed rocks are folded to some degree. Folds vary in size from millimetre to kilometre scale.

Colour

Metamorphic rocks are commonly light to dark grey, but there are several exceptions with a distinctive colour that is useful in identification. Quartzite and pure marble can be recognized by their sparkling white colour, and mica shists are characterized by shiny flakes of silver or black mica. Glaucophane schists are slate blue, while eclogites are a striking red and green. Serpentinites are also distinctive, with red and green streaks or blotches and a waxy appearance.

Mineralogy

The total number of minerals appearing in a metamorphic rock is called the *assemblage* and is usually relatively few, especially if the rock had *equilibrated*, that is, recrystallization was completed. The type of minerals that appear in a particular grade of metamorphic rock depends on the composition of the original rock.

Sedimentary rocks

Sediments which form rocks originate through physical or chemical processes, or through the accumulation of organic remains. The sediments may then be buried, compacted and converted into rocks, a process known as *lithification*. The most common sedimentary rock type is formed

Around these hot springs in Turkey, the mineral-rich water precipitates calcite, as travertine. This has created a series of terraces.

Introduction

from *detrital* or *clastic sediments*. These are produced where existing rocks are weathered and eroded, mainly by the mechanical actions of rain, rivers, wind and glaciers, together with the chemical action of water and dissolved materials. Water, wind or moving ice then transport the fragments and deposit them as *sediments*. Water-borne material is deposited in rivers, in lakes or the sea. These sediments accumulate up to several kilometres thick. On burial they are compacted by overlying material and may be cemented by percolating waters to form a rock.

The second most common sedimentary rock type is formed by the accumulation of organic matter from plants or animals. The most abundant organic sediment is derived from the calcium carbonate skeletons of marine animals such as shells and corals, forming limestones. Coal and oil are economically important sediments formed from organic matter.

The third type of sedimentary rocks are *evaporites*, formed by the precipitation of salts in hot dry regions from shallow seas and lakes.

Texture

The main textural feature of detrital rocks is the grain size, which refers to particles making up the sediment. They vary enormously, from boulders to microscopic clay particles. Grain size is classified by the following grades: *coarse* – more than 2mm (0.08in) in gravels; *medium* – 0.0625 to 2mm (0.02 – 0.08in) in sands; *fine* – 0.0039 to 0.0625mm (0.0015 – 0.02in) in silt; and less than 0.0039mm (0.0015in) in clay. Fine-grained rocks are called *argillaceous*, medium-grained, *arenaceous* and coarse-grained, *rudaceous*. Extensive transport of detrital grains by water produces rounded grains, and continued reworking by currents as in beach areas sorts them into roughly the same size. Thus a sediment with rounded, well-sorted grains is called *mature*, while one with angular grains that range widely in size is called *immature*. The latter is unlikely to have been transported far from its source area. Wind-blown grains are often polished and almost spherical.

rudaceous texture

arenaceous texture

argillaceous texture

Structure

Sedimentary structures are usually very apparent in such rocks and are useful in understanding the environment in which deposition occurred.

Bedding is layering in the rock which can be picked out by varying textures, colours and mineralogies. It reflects episodes of rapid deposition followed by relatively little. Beds can vary in thickness.

Those ranging in thickness from several metres down to centimetre size are called *strata*. Those less than a centimetre thick are called *laminations*. The surface between layers is called the *bedding plane*. Although beds may be deposited horizontally, they are often tilted or folded by later Earth movements. Faulting is easily seen as the displacement of bedding planes.

Current bedding forms overlapping wedges. It is caused by deposition, often of sand, on a surface sloping in the direction of the current. The current may be of wind or water, and such bedding may range from a centimetre thick if formed in weak water currents, up to the size of a sand dune.

graded bedding

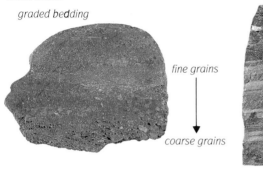

fine grains

↓

coarse grains

bedding

Graded bedding displays a variation of grain size within a bed from coarse at the bottom to fine at the top. This occurs when a mass of sediment has been deposited quickly, without sorting, so that the larger grains fall most rapidly, as in greywackes. Graded bedding indicates which way up the beds were formed in highly folded rocks.

Ripple marks are the lines of ridges formed by water or wind movement preserved on the bedding plane at the top of a stratum.

Unconformities reflect the gaps in the sedimentary record between periods of deposition. They sometimes represent hundreds of millions of years during which the underlying rocks were often faulted and/or folded, then eroded. When new beds are deposited on these older strata, the surface between them is apparent as an unconformity. If the time interval was short, the underlying rocks may have remained horizontal and so the unconformity may not be obvious in the field.

Colour

The colour of a sedimentary rock is of limited use in identification. Pure limestones are usually white or near to white. But most sediments are coloured to varying degrees by iron oxides (red) or by organic material (grey to black).

Mineralogy

The identification of minerals in sedimentary rocks is less important for classification than in igneous or metamorphic rocks. Most important is to recognize calcite in order to identify limestones, and to distinguish silica from feldspars when identifying sandstones.

Introduction

COLLECTING ROCKS AND MINERALS

Collecting rocks and minerals is a fascinating and rewarding hobby, and can be done either on your own or with others. Local libraries often have information about a local geological society where enthusiasts meet.

Equipment

To study rocks and minerals, some basic equipment is required. First, you will need a good hand lens, with a magnification of about × 10, and a geological hammer for field work. This should have a square head and a pick or chisel edge. A chisel may be useful for splitting open rocks. Always wear safety goggles when hammering, to protect your eyes from splinters of rock. It is advisable to wear a hard hat in certain areas and is essential if visiting a quarry. Sensible clothes are needed, including walking boots or shoes, and a small rucksack to transport your finds.

Each specimen should be numbered instantly using a felt tip pen, either directly, or on a label stuck on the specimen. The number should be entered into a notebook, together with notes on the locality, the date, and so on. Wrap specimens in newspaper to avoid chipping.

Where to start looking

A local museum is a good place to start, because it often contains representative samples of local materials. Once you decide to go on a collecting expedition, study a local geological map. This will not only guide you to interesting rocks but may also help you to avoid major misidentifications, which newcomers to the field can make all too easily. Also, study the topography so that you can set out suitably clothed. Make sure someone knows where you are going, especially in rugged terrain.

Good places to start are road cuttings, cliffs, quarries or stream beds. Take care to ask permission before venturing onto private land. When possible, collect from mine dumps, or from rock fallen from cliffs rather than indiscriminately hammering at fresh faces. Quite often the best specimens are found in this way.

Looking after your collection

Insoluble specimens may be cleaned with water and a little detergent using a soft brush. Each specimen should be given a permanent number written onto the specimen in Indian ink, or onto a spot of white acrylic paint. The specimen details and number should then be entered into a catalogue. It is then ready for display or storage. If you have difficulty in identifying a specimen, your local museum will be happy to help.

A word of caution

Enthusiastic but inexperienced collectors almost always return from an expedition overladen with samples that are subsequently discarded as duplicates. Make sure that you collect only what you really need, and do not leave sharp fragments of rock lying about that might damage vehicle tyres or livestock. Some sites have now become so overworked that hammering is no longer permitted.

Glossary

Acid (of igneous rocks) containing at least 10 per cent quartz, and chemically more than 65 per cent silica.

Aeolian wind-blown.

Alkaline (of igneous rock) with a high content of alkali metals, namely sodium and potassium.

Amygdales vesicles found in volcanic rocks, originally formed by gas bubbles in the magma and later filled with secondary minerals.

An percentage of anorthite in plagioclase feldspar.

Arenaceous (of sedimentary rocks) with sand-sized grains (see p.28).

Argillaceous (of sedimentary rocks) fine-grained (see p.28).

Aureole country rock affected by contact metamorphism around an igneous intrusion (see p.26).

Basic (of igneous rocks) containing 45-55 per cent silica.

Batholith large intrusion, often with no visible floor, up to 1000 km² (386 sq mi) in area.

Bioherm mound of organic remains in a reef, also called a reef knoll.

Biostrome laterally extensive reefs made up of shells.

Cementation deposition of cement (usually silica, calcite or iron hydrates) between the particles in a loose sediment, thus converting it to hard rock.

Clay minerals fine-grained, hydrous silicates formed by extensive weathering of other silicate minerals.

Columnar joints vertical joints common in basalts producing regular, hexagonal pillars of rock.

Concretion irregular or rounded mass formed by the precipitation of a new mineral within a sedimentary rock. Rounded forms are called nodules.

Craton area of the continental crust that has not been significantly deformed typically since Cambrian times. Cratons contain extensive crystalline basement rocks called shields.

Cross-stratification phenomenon occurring in ripples, sand waves and dunes where individual strata are laid down at an angle to the main bedding planes. Also known as cross, current, or false bedding.

Detrital (of sedimentary rocks) formed by the accumulation of rock fragments. Also called clastic (see p.28).

Diatom single-celled plant found in oceans and lakes with a skeleton composed of silica.

Druse irregularly shaped cavity containing minerals that project inwards from the cavity walls.

Dune bedding large-scale cross stratification formed by the movement of sand dunes. Usually several metres high.

Dyke vertical or near-vertical igneous intrusion that cuts across existing bedding or foliation in the host rock (see p.23).

Essential minerals minerals which define a rock and must be present in order to give it a particular name (see p.24).

Facies group of metamorphic rocks formed under a particular set of physical conditions from any rock type. Rocks of the greenschist, amphibolite and granulite facies are all formed at moderate pressures (depths of 10–30km), but at low, medium and high temperatures respectively.

Fault break in the rocks resulting in displacement either side.

Feldspathoids aluminosilicate minerals, similar to the feldspars but containing less silica.

Felsic (of rocks) essentially composed of the light-coloured minerals feldspar and either feldspathoid or silica.

Ferromagnesian dark coloured iron- and/or magnesium-bearing minerals, including augite, biotite, hornblende and olivine (see p.24).

Glossary

Flow texture   alignment of needle-like or tabular crystals, formed when crystallization occurs while the molten rock is still flowing.

Fumarole   small volcanic vent issuing gases but no lava.

Graded bedding   with coarse grains at the bottom of the bed, grading to finer particles at the top (see p.29).

Granitoid   group of plutonic igneous rocks containing quartz. Includes granodiorite and tonalite.

Granular texture   comprising minerals of roughly equal size.

Graphic texture   intergrowth of minerals, especially quartz and feldspar, resembling runic inscriptions.

Hydrothermal deposit   minerals which crystallize from hot watery fluids in the late stages of formation of igneous rocks.

Intermediate   (of igneous rocks) with a silica content of 52–65 per cent, including syenite, trachyte, diorite and andesite.

Joints   cracks and fissures in rocks with no displacement either side.

Lamination   fine layering in sediments, only millimetres thick. Often forms the internal structure in beds.

Lithic   pertaining to rocks.

Lithification   alteration of loose sediments into a rock (see p.27).

Mafic   (of rocks) essentially composed of dark-coloured minerals.

Marine transgression   rise in sea level, causing submersion of a land mass and the deposition of marine sediment. Conversely, marine regression causes deposition to cease and erosion to commence.

Marl   mudrock composed of roughly equal amounts of clay and calcite.

Matrix   fine-grained material surrounding coarser grains. Also known as groundmass.

Metabasite   metamorphosed basic rock.

Metapelite   metamorphosed pelitic rock.

Metasediment   metamorphosed sedimentary rock.

Metasomatism   process which alters the composition of a mineral or rock by the addition or subtraction of chemical elements by the action of hot fluids (see p.20).

Ophiolite   suite of rocks comprising pillow lavas, dykes, gabbros and ultrabasic rocks, thought to have formed from oceanic crust and now exposed at the surface (see p.23).

Ophitic   (of igneous rocks) special type of poikilitic texture in which plagioclase is enclosed by pyroxene.

Orbicular texture   concentric shells of a different texture and/or mineralogy from the parent rock.

Orogenic belt   belt of rocks commonly characterized by deformation and folding, formed in a mountain-building episode.

Pelagic   of the deep sea. Usually clays or oozes composed of tiny silica or calcium carbonate skeletons.

Pelitic   (of rocks) characterized by a high aluminium and low calcium ontent especially clays and shales.

Perlitic   (of glassy rocks) containing irregular, spheroidal cracks which are formed by contraction during cooling.

Phenocrysts   large igneous crystals which contrast markedly in size with the surrounding crystals (see p.23).

Phytoplankton   small floating plants such as diatoms.

Plug   roughly vertical and cylindrical volcanic intrusion.

Pluton   large, coarse-grained igneous intrusion (see p.22).

Pneumatolysis   reaction of the hot gases given off by a cooling magma with the surrounding country rock (see p.20).

Poikilitic   (of igneous rocks) where large crystals of the host rock enclose small

Glossary

andomly oriented crystals of a different mineral.

oikiloblastic (of metamorphic rocks) where a large crystal contains small inclusions of another mineral (see p.26).

orphyritic (of igneous rocks) comprising large crystals (phenocrysts) set in a finer-grained or glassy groundmass.

orphyroblast large, well-developed crystal that has grown in a metamorphic rock (see p.26).

yroclast fragment of volcanic rock scattered by explosive eruption.

adiolaria single-celled marine animals with a skeleton of silica.

elict structure structure of the original rock which has persisted through metamorphism (see p.26).

ipple marks small-scale undulations found in the bedding planes of sandstones and siltstones (see p.29).

udaceous (of sedimentary rocks) refers to the coarsest clastic sediments, specifically gravels, conglomerates and breccias (see p.28).

hields areas of crystalline basement rock associated with cratons.

ill essentially horizontal, sheet-like igneous intrusion usually between two sedimentary beds, may be hundreds of metres thick.

lump bedding produced when an overlying bed slumps down into a weak underlying bed.

olid solution series of minerals where there is complete gradation in composition between end members.

pherulites spherical or sub-spherical bodies with a radial arrangement of acicular crystals, often of feldspar.

pilite fine-grained, basic igneous rocks richer in sodium and water than basalt, and containing albite rather than plagioclase.

tock small batholith, with an area of less than 10 km^2 (see p.23).

ubhedral grains showing some crystal faces.

ublimation process whereby a solid turns directly into a vapour on heating, without passing through a liquid phase.

ubophitic (of igneous rocks) with feldspar crystals partly enclosed by pyroxene crystals of the same size.

uccession series of sedimentary rocks deposited in sequence.

uite group of rocks that are related to each other by a common origin or process.

ectonism large-scale movements and deformation of the Earth's crust.

ltrabasic (of igneous rocks) containing less than 45 silica.

ltramafic (of igneous rocks) containing more than 90 per cent dark minerals.

nconformity surface between sedimentary strata representing a time gap between periods of deposition.

acuoles spaces left by materials in a magma that are easily vaporized, such as water and carbon dioxide.

ein irregular network of foreign minerals deposited in a rock.

enolith piece of rock that is different in origin to the igneous rock surrounding it (see p.24).

ooplankton small floating animals such as radiolarians.

Gold _Au_

Gold has long been prized. Its value lies in its characteristic yellow colour, its rarity and its ability to be worked. It also has a high degree of resistance to chemical reactions, a property which makes it one of the so-called 'noble' metals. It does not dissolve in acids, apart from _aqua regia_. The old symbol for gold was a circle, a reflection of its ancient identity with the Sun. Gold is used in jewellery and was used in coinage. It has uses in plating, scientific instruments, medicine and dentistry. The largest gold nugget recorded was 214 kg (472 lb). It was found in 1872 at Holterman's Reef, New South Wales, Australia. The world's leading gold producers are South Africa and the Soviet Union. Many people mistake pyrite (fool's gold) and chalcopyrite for gold, but these minerals are harder and more brittle than gold.

Gold nugget

Gold nugget

Gold in quartz

	GOLD		
*Colour	characteristic yellow	*Alteration	none
*Lustre	metallic	Occurrence	in hydrothermal veins often associated with quartz; in alluvial deposits, notably stream or river sediments, where it is separated from other minerals by virtue of its greater density; alluvial deposits may consolidate into rock
Transparency	opaque; transmits greenish light in the thinnest sheets		
Streak	yellow, lighter when alloyed with silver		
*Hardness	2.5 – 3		
Cleavage	none		
Fracture	hackly; malleable		
Habit	usually dendritic (branching) growths or disseminated grains; occasionally rounded nuggets and rarely octahedral, dodecahedral or cubic crystals	Examples	Witwatersrand (South Africa), Yukon (Canada), Porcupine (Canada), the Mother Lode, California, (USA) and the USSR; very little in Europe, although used to be mined in a small way near Monte Rosa (Italy)
Twinning	common on octahedron		
Specific gravity	19.3		
Other tests	insoluble in single acids		
Crystal system	cubic		

_Ag_ Silver

ilver is a metal that is prized for much
he same reasons as gold, although it is
omewhat more chemically reactive. It
s widely distributed but in small
mounts, being rarer than gold.
hroughout history, craftsmen have
ade silver jewellery – silver beads
ound in Egypt date back around 6000
ears. Silver was also used for coins
efore copper-nickel alloy came into
se. Silver is the best known reflector of
ght, which makes it useful in plating.
ts extremely high electrical
onductivity ensures a high demand in
lectronics. The instability of silver
alides to light forms the basis of
lassical photographic techniques. The
ld symbol for silver was the Moon.

Silver on calcite

Silver

Wiry form

	SILVER		
*Colour	silver-white	***Alteration**	tarnishes to black sulphide
Lustre	metallic	**Occurrence**	in the oxidized zone of
Transparency	opaque; very high reflectivity		hydrothermal sulphide veins,
	(95 per cent)		and as primary ore in such
Streak	silver-white		veins
Hardness	2.5 – 3	**Examples**	best known primary silver
Cleavage	none		deposit is at Kongsberg
Fracture	hackly; malleable		(Norway); other well-known
Habit	commonly in a wiry form or		deposits include the
	as scales; crystals very rare		Comstock Lode, Nevada
Twinning	common		(USA), Freiberg (Germany)
Specific gravity	10.5		and San Luis Potosí
Other tests	dissolves in nitric acid and		(Mexico)
	then precipitates white silver		
	chloride on addition of		
	common salt or hydrochloric		
	acid; very good conductor of		
	electricity and heat		
Crystal system	cubic		

Copper *Cu*

Although it usually occurs in small quantities, native copper is widely distributed. This fact, together with its malleability and resistance to weathering, explains why it has long been used to make ornaments, tools and weapons. Bronze, an alloy of copper and tin which is much harder than pure copper, was first used in large quantities around 3000 BC. Brass, an alloy of copper and zinc, is a popular metal because of its attractive polished finish. Because copper is cheap, ductile (pliant) and a good conductor of electricity, it is widely used in the electrical industry. The name comes from the word for Cyprus, where copper has been mined since ancient times.

malachite coating

Copper

Branching form

Copper with tarnish

Massive form

tarnish

	COPPER		
*Colour	light rose on fresh surface	**Occurrence**	as hydrothermal and metasomatic deposits; it fills cracks and amygdales in basaltic lava flows as well as partially replacing other minerals therein especially those containing iron; also found as part of the cement in conglomerates and sandstones
Lustre	metallic		
Transparency	opaque		
Streak	metallic copper-red		
*Hardness	2.5–3		
Cleavage	none		
Fracture	hackly; malleable, ductile		
Habit	usually dendritic or wiry; rare crystals usually cubic or dodecahedral		
Twinning	common	**Examples**	best crystals are found in the Keweenawan Peninsula, Lake Superior (USA) where huge masses occur; others include Monte Catini (Italy), Bisbee, Arizona, Franklin, New Jersey (USA) and Lang-ban (Sweden) and in Chile, Germany, USSR and Zambia
Specific gravity	8.95		
Other tests	readily soluble in nitric acid		
Crystal system	cubic		
*Alteration	slight alteration gives characteristic copper-red colour; black copper oxide gives a dull brown colour; green carbonate on exposed surfaces		

_Pt_ Platinum

Platinum is a rare and precious metal that occurs as a native element. It resembles silver, but it is less reactive and does not tarnish in air. Its greater hardness, higher density and high melting point – 1769°C (3216°F) against 962°C (1764°F) – also distinguish it from silver. These properties, together with its malleability and thermal stability make it useful for laboratory tongs and crucibles, electrical contacts in thermo couples, and for jewellry. Platinum is also an exceptionally good catalyst, used in the chemical and petroleum industries. Like gold, another noble metal, the only common acid combination to dissolve it is hot _aqua regia_, a mixture of concentrated hydrochloric and nitric acids. Native platinum contains lesser amounts of other related native elements, namely iridium, osmium, palladium and rhodium. The refining of platinum is the principle source of these other 'heavy metals'. Platinum derives its name from the Spanish _platina_, a diminutive form of _plata_, meaning 'silver'.

Platinum nugget

Platinum grains

	PLATINUM
Colour	grey-white to light grey
Lustre	metallic
Transparency	opaque
Streak	white, steel-grey
Hardness	4 – 4.5
Cleavage	absent
Fracture	hackly; ductile
Habit	rare cubic crystals; usually as grains, scales or nuggets
*Specific gravity	21.5 when pure; natural material usually 14 –19, mainly due to dissolved iron and copper
Other tests	insoluble in single acids; occasionally magnetic
Crystal system	cubic
*Alteration	none
Occurrence	segregations, alongside chromite in ultrabasic igneous rocks, especially dunites; in norites with immiscible sulphide deposits; as placer deposits in stream or river sediments, separated by its high density; non-native platinum occurs in the mineral sperrylite ($PtAs_2$)
Examples	segregations in the Bushveld Complex (South Africa) and the Ural Mountains (USSR); with sulphide deposits in Sudbury (Canada); placer deposits in the Nizhne Tagilsk region of the Urals (USSR), in Colombia and the USA

Arsenic As

Arsenic is a fairly rare mineral which is found in hydrothermal veins in association with silver-cobalt-nickel ores. In this form, it rarely occurs in sufficient quantity to make extraction viable. However, it occurs widely in combination, particularly in sulphide ores. Most commercial arsenic is obtained from other arsenic-bearing minerals such as arsenopyrite. The oxide As_2O_3 (white arsenic) is the most widely used form of arsenic. It is obtained from the flue-dust produced in the smelting of arsenic ores. From about 2000 BC, metal-workers have used about 4 per cent arsenic in copper goods to make them harder and stronger. Arsenic is still used in some special alloys. It is poisonous which makes it useful in pesticides, preservatives and, in the pharmaceutical industry, for treating parasitic illnesses. It derives its name from the Greek word *arsenikon* meaning 'masculine', because metals were believed to be different sexes. The term was first applied to the mineral orpiment because of its potent properties.

Mammilated form

Concentrically layered mass

ARSENIC		Occurrence	in hydrothermal veins usually associated with ores of silver, cobalt and nickel, in igneous and metamorphic rocks
Colour	light grey, tarnishing rapidly to dark grey		
Lustre	metallic	**Examples**	Gikos, Siberia (USSR), Erzgebirge and the Harz Moutains (Germany), Washington Camp, Santa Cruz County (USA), France, Italy, Romania, Czechoslovakia
Transparency	opaque		
Streak	light grey		
Hardness	3.5		
Cleavage	basal, perfect		
Fracture	uneven; brittle		
Habit	crystals rare (artificial ones pseudo-cubic); generally granular, massive or concentrically layered botryoidal or stalactitic masses		
Twinning	rare		
Specific gravity	5.7		
***Other tests**	smells like garlic on heating or striking with a hammer		
Crystal system	trigonal		

_Sb_ **Antimony**

Native antimony is found only in small quantities in hydrothermal veins, where it is formed by reactions of antimony–sulphur minerals. As antimony occurs rarely as a native element, the economic sources of this metal are ores, mainly stibnite (Sb_2S_3). Antimony is alloyed with lead to make type-metal and bullets, because it lowers the melting point and increases the hardness of the lead. Alloyed with copper and tin, it produces low-friction Babbitt metal, used for bearings. Antimony and its compounds are poisonous and are used in drugs for the treatment of parasitic diseases. The name comes from the Latin _antimonium_. The chemical symbol for antimony, Sb, comes from the Latin _stiborum_, meaning 'mark'. Black stibnite has been used at least since Ancient Egyptian times as mascara for painting eyebrows and eyelashes.

Antimony

Massive form

	ANTIMONY	
Colour	light grey	
Lustre	metallic	
Transparency	opaque	
Streak	grey	
Hardness	3–3.5	
Cleavage	basal, perfect; rhombohedral, good	
Fracture	uneven; very brittle	
Habit	crystals rare; usually massive and reniform (kidney-shaped); sometimes lamellar with a cleavage through the mass	
Twinning	common, repeated	
Specific gravity	6.6–6.7	
Crystal system	trigonal	
Occurrence	in hydrothermal veins often accompanying silver or arsenic; associated minerals	

are stibnite, sphalerite, galena and pyrite

Examples Sala (Sweden), Andreasberg (Germany), Coimbra (Portugal), Val Cavargna and Sardinia (Italy), New Brunswick (Canada), Kern County, California (USA), Saranoak (Borneo)

Bismuth *Bi*

Bismuth is a semi-metal that occurs rarely as a native element. It is related to arsenic and antimony in structure and has similar physical properties. They are all brittle and are poorer conductors of heat and electricity than metals. Bismuth is not of great economic importance, most of that produced is used for medicines and cosmetics. It is also used with cadmium, lead or tin to make low-melting alloys, such as Wood's metal which melts at 70°C (158°F). Such alloys are useful in electrical fuses and fire protection devices. Like antimony, bismuth is also used for fine castings. Artificially produced crystals of bismuth can be attractive because of their good cleavage and form, together with their high lustre. Bismuth is produced mainly as a by-product from the smelting of sulphide ores.

oxide coating

Bismuth

Native form

Small globules on matrix

	BISMUTH
*Colour	silver-white, tarnishing to reddish tinge, sometimes iridescent
Lustre	metallic
Transparency	opaque
Streak	silver-white, shiny
Hardness	2–2.5
*Cleavage	basal, perfect
Fracture	uneven; sectile
Habit	crystals rare; massive, granular or in branching, net-like forms
Twinning	common, repeated
Specific gravity	9.7–9.8
*Other tests	melts readily at 271°C (520°F), giving an orange-yellow oxide coating; dissolves in nitric acid
Crystal system	trigonal

Occurrence	in hydrothermal veins, often associated with gold, silver, tin, nickel, cobalt and lead
Examples	Oruro and Tasna (Bolivia), Cornwall (England), Erzgebirge (Germany), Kongsberg (Norway), Ontario (Canada); small amounts at Monroe, Connecticut and in Summit and Boulder counties, Colorado (USA)

Diamond is composed of pure carbon, like graphite. But the atoms in diamond have been forced into a compact three-dimensional structure by the high pressures in the upper mantle, where it is formed. Hence diamond is much harder and has a higher specific gravity than graphite. This is reflected in its name, which comes from the Greek word for 'invincible'. Gem-quality diamonds are colourless, transparent and unflawed. Low-quality diamonds are used as industrial abrasives. Varieties of diamond are *bort*, which has a rounded, fibrous, radiate structure, and *carbonado*, which is black and microcrystalline. Diamond is mined from kimberlite and alluvial deposits. The largest recorded diamond is the Cullinan, from the Transvaal in South Africa. Uncut it weighed 3106 carats (1 carat equals 0.2 g or 0.007 oz).

Cut and polished diamond

Diamond in kimberlite

DIAMOND			
Colour	colourless, but may be coloured by yellow, red, brown, grey or black impurities	**Twinning**	sometimes, on octahedron
		Specific gravity	3.5
		Crystal system	cubic
*Lustre	brilliantly adamantine to greasy	**Occurrence**	rare and in ultrabasic rocks of deep origin called kimberlites which form roughly cylindrical pipes or sometime dykes, found in continental shield areas; also found in deposits in rivers running from such rocks
Transparency	transparent, but can be translucent to opaque when very dark coloured and of poor crystallinity		
Streak	white		
*Hardness	10	**Examples**	most important diamond fields are those of Kimberley, Transvaal (South Africa); other good quality diamonds in Tanzania, Yakutia (USSR), India and Brazil; also worked in the sea bed off Namibia
*Cleavage	octahedral, perfect		
Fracture	conchoidal		
Habit	octahedral crystals often with curved faces, sometimes dodecahedral, rarely tetrahedral; frequently of flattened habit		

Graphite c

Graphite, like diamond, is a form of pure carbon. The carbon atoms in graphite are joined together in hexagonal arrays in two-dimensional sheets stacked one on top of another. This gives graphite its characteristic basal cleavage and flaking, which imparts a greasy feel and gives it lubricant properties. Graphite is also known as plumbago or black lead. Its softness and black streak have long made it a writing tool, especially in pencils. It is also used in crucibles, electrodes, generator brushes, and as a moderator to slow down neutrons in atomic reactors. Its colour, streak and lower specific gravity distinguish it from molybdenite. Graphite is formed mainly when sediments rich in organic matter are metamorphosed.

cleavage surfaces

Graphite

Graphite

Graphite

	GRAPHITE	
Colour	black	
Lustre	dull, metallic	
Transparency	opaque	
***Streak**	black, shiny	
Hardness	1–2	
***Cleavage**	basal, perfect	
Habit	usually as scales and foliated or earthy masses or as compact lumps; occasionally as six-sided flat, tabular crystals	
***Specific gravity**	2.1–2.2	
***Other tests**	greasy feel; thin flakes broken off along cleavage are flexible; conducts electricity	
Crystal system	hexagonal	
Occurrence	mainly in metamorphosed sediments, usually marbles, schists and gneisses; also in metamorphosed coal; sometimes associated with basic igneous rocks, pegmatites and quartz veins possibly from volcanic gases; also in meteorites	
Examples	production mainly in USSR, Mexico, Korea, Austria, Sri Lanka and Madagascar; in Europe, economic deposits in Czechoslovakia, Germany and Val Chisone (Italy). Crystals in marble at Ogdensburg, New York and in gneiss at Edison, New Jersey (USA)	

Sulphur is a soft, low-density mineral that has a bright yellow colour when pure. Although still obtained from natural deposits, much sulphur is now produced as a by-product in oil refining. Sulphur is used in the manufacture of sulphuric acid, gunpowder, insecticides and matches. It is also the vulcanizing (hardening) agent for rubber. Sulphur crystals belong to the orthorhombic crystal system, the finest examples coming from Sicily and the Romagna, Italy. Sulphur also occurs in two other crystal forms belonging to the monoclinic crystal system, ß-sulphur and γ-sulphur. Both of these are formed at higher temperatures. They rarely occur naturally. The name is thought to come from the Indo-European words meaning 'to burn slowly'.

Sulphur crystals

Massive sulphur

resinous lustre

Sulphur crystals

SULPHUR

*Colour	bright yellow to yellow-brown
Lustre	resinous
Transparency	transparent to translucent
Streak	white
*Hardness	1.5–2.5
Cleavage	none
Fracture	uneven to conchoidal
Habit	bipyramids or thick tablets; also encrusting, stalactitic, massive or powdery
Specific gravity	2–2.1
*Other tests	low melting point, 113°C (235°F); burns with a bluish flame to give the choking and toxic gas sulphur dioxide; soluble in carbon disulphide
Crystal system	orthorhombic
Occurrence	encrustations around volcanic vents and fumaroles caused by sublimation; precipitates in hot springs caused by reaction of the dissolved gases H_2S and SO_2; associated with gypsum and bituminous materials in Tertiary shales, sandstones and limestones; in the cap rock of salt domes
Examples	mostly produced in Louisiana and Texas (USA) from salt domes and in Sicily from Tertiary sediments. Volcanic sulphur deposits in Japan, Indonesia and the South American Andes

Pyrite FeS_2

Commonly known as 'fool's gold', pyrite is an abundant and widespread mineral. Its name comes from the Greek word for fire and refers to the sparks produced when pyrite is struck with a hammer. It is brass-yellow in colour, paler than gold and chalcopyrite, but slightly darker than marcasite. The ancient Greeks used pyrite for earrings and pins and the Incas may have used pyrite tablets as mirrors. It has been used since Victorian times in jewellery, though jewellers often call it marcasite. It was formerly used instead of flint in old wheel lock firearms. Pyrite is commonly mined for the copper and gold associated with it, but its chief use is as a source of sulphur, which is used in the manufacture of sulphuric acid and ferrous sulphate. This mineral is also known as pyrites or iron pyrites.

Pyrite nodule

Pyritohedron

Pyrite and quartz

Cubic crystals in slate

striations

	PYRITE		
*Colour	bronze yellow to pale brass yellow, uniform; lacks tarnish	**Specific gravity**	4.9–5.1
Lustre	metallic	**Other tests**	emits sparks when struck; powder dissolves in nitric but not hydrochloric acid
Transparency	opaque		
Streak	greenish or brownish black	**Crystal system**	cubic
Hardness	6–6.5	**Alteration**	readily oxidizes to iron sulphate or the hydrated oxide limonite
Cleavage	indistinct, cubic and octahedral		
Fracture	conchoidal to uneven; brittle	**Occurrence**	in sedimentary rocks, especially black shales; often replaces fossils; an accessory mineral in igneous rocks; common in ore veins; in metamorphic rocks, especially slate
Habit	as cubic crystals, often striated parallel to cube edges, also as octahedra and pyrithedra; massive, as granular aggregates or nodules with internally radiating structure		
Twinning	frequent, looking like interpenetrating cubes, known as 'Iron Crosses'	**Examples**	Rio Tinto (Spain), Gavorrano (Italy), Sulitjelma (Norway), Elba, Cyprus, Mount Lyell (Tasmania), Leadville and Gilman, Colorado (USA)

FeS_2 Marcasite

Ancient writers used the term marcasite, which is of Arabic or Moorish origin, for bismuth and antimony. Later, mineralogists and miners used it as the name for pyrite and even today the so-called marcasite used for brooches and earrings is actually pyrite. Marcasite is very similar in appearance and of identical composition to pyrite. Its main distinguishing features are its paler colour (hence the alternative name 'white iron pyrites'), its lower specific gravity and its crystal system. 'Spearhead' forms of marcasite are characteristic. In the past, polished marcasite was used to make ornaments.

Spear – shaped twinned crystal

Aggregate of crystals

Aggregate of crystals

	MARCASITE	**Crystal system**	orthorhombic
*Colour	pale bronze-yellow to silvery on fresh surfaces	**Alteration**	decomposes to iron sulphate or limonite more readily than pyrite; may alter to pyrite; eventually crumbles to dust
Lustre	metallic		
Transparency	opaque		
Streak	greyish or brownish black	**Occurrence**	formed under acid conditions, at lower temperatures than pyrite; in hydrothermal veins, often with lead and zinc ores; also as a precipitate in nodules in sedimentary rocks e.g. chalk; may replace fossils
Hardness	6–6.5		
Cleavage	poor, prismatic		
Fracture	uneven; brittle		
Habit	as tabular crystals, often with curved faces; also massive, stalactitic or nodular, with internally radiating structure		
*Twinning	commonly twinned to form 'cockscomb' aggregates and 'spearhead' forms	**Examples**	Derbyshire (England), Carlsbad and Rammelsberg (Germany), Karlovy Vary (Czechoslovakia); Romania and the Tri-State mining district (USA)
Specific gravity	4.8–4.9		
Other tests	dissolves with difficulty in nitric acid, flakes of sulphur appearing in solution		

Arsenopyrite *FeAsS*

Arsenopyrite, also known as mispickel or arsenical pyrites, is the principal ore of arsenic and the most abundant arsenic mineral. Of widespread occurrence, its appearance is paler and more silvery than pyrite, with which it is commonly found. Its colour also distinguishes arsenopyrite from marcasite. It may tarnish, however, when exposed. It occurs in sulphide deposits associated with gold and cobalt, in a pegmatitic or pneumatolytic environment with tin and copper, and in high-temperature hydrothermal veins with gold, silver and nickel. Some varieties may contain traces of other metals. Cobalt, gold, silver and tin are by-products of the smelting process.

Crystals

Crystals

Massive form

	ARSENOPYRITE
*Colour	silvery-white to steel-grey, tarnishing pale copper-colour on exposure
Lustre	metallic
Transparency	opaque
*Streak	black or dark grey
Hardness	5.5–6
Cleavage	good, parallel to dome faces
Fracture	uneven; brittle
Habit	forms elongated, striated prismatic crystals; may appear orthorhombic through twinning; also massive, as columnar aggregates; compact and granular
Twinning	cross-shaped twins common
Specific gravity	5.9–6.2
*Other tests	sparks when struck with a hammer, giving off garlic fumes; soluble in nitric acid, giving sulphur; fuses easily, giving off a strong garlic smell
Crystal system	monoclinic
Occurrence	in sulphide deposits; also disseminated in limestones and dolomites; in pegmatites and hydrothermal veins; in small amounts in concretionary layers of siderite in black band ironstone
Examples	important deposits occur at Sulitjelma (Norway), Boliden (Sweden), Freiberg (Germany). Also found at Roxbury, Connecticut and Leadville, Colorado (USA) and Hastings County, Ontario (Canada)

Realgar is an orange-red mineral which can be distinguished from others of a similar colour by its streak. Realgar commonly occurs with lemon-yellow orpiment (As_2S_3), to which it readily alters. The term realgar comes from the Arabic *rahj al ghar* (meaning 'powder of the mine'), while the name orpiment is a corruption of the Latin *auripigmentum* (golden paint) – a reference not only to its colour, but also to the belief that it contained gold. Realgar is used in the manufacture of fireworks and paint. Orpiment is an ore of arsenic, occurring in arsenic veins, hot springs and volcanic deposits. It is used in tanning hides to remove hair.

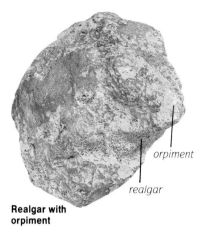

orpiment

realgar

Realgar with orpiment

Orpiment

Realgar crystals

	REALGAR	**Crystal system**	monoclinic
*Colour	orange to orange-red	**Alteration**	decomposes on exposure to light and air to an orange-yellow powder of orpiment and arsenolite (AsS_2O_3)
*Lustre	resinous		
Transparency	transparent to translucent		
*Streak	orange to red		
Hardness	1.5 – 2	**Occurrence**	in low-temperature ore veins associated with orpiment, stibnite or cinnabar; also in some limestones and clay rocks; occurs in volcanic lavas and as a hot spring deposit
Cleavage	good in one direction		
Fracture	conchoidal or uneven; sectile		
Habit	usually massive, in compact aggregates or as a scarlet incrustation; rarely as vertically striated, short prismatic crystals		
Specific gravity	3.5 – 3.6	**Examples**	Binnenthal (Switzerland), Naples and Vesuvius (Italy), Matra (Corsica), Nagyag (Romania), Yellowstone National Park, Wyoming and King County, Washington (USA)
*Other tests	fuses easily, giving off arsenic fumes with a garlic smell; decomposed by nitric acid; association with orpiment		

Chalcopyrite _CuFeS₂_

Chalcopyrite or copper pyrites, is a brassy yellow, metallic mineral. It is one of the more common sulphides and the most common copper mineral. It can be distinguished from pyrite because it is usually deeper in colour, and, unlike pyrite, it crumbles when cut with a knife, and does not produce sparks when hit with a hammer. Unlike the similar pyrrhotite, it is non-magnetic. Its brittleness, streak and solubility in nitric acid distinguish it from gold. It is a major copper ore, producing four-fifths of the world's copper, and gold and silver as useful by-products. It occurs with bornite in sulphide deposits of the Copper Belt in Zambia, and also as grains in shale in the well-known Kupferschiefer of Mansfeld, Germany.

Massive form

Chalcopyrite with quartz

Chalcopyrite

	CHALCOPYRITE		
*Colour	brass-yellow, often with a brown or iridescent tarnish	Occurrence	exposure to moisture in high- and medium-temperature veins with cassiterite, or galena and sphalerite, and as a 'porphyry copper' deposit in mafic volcanic rocks; in contact metamorphic rocks (skarns) and in placer deposits formed from the break-up of these rocks
Lustre	metallic		
Transparency	opaque		
*Streak	greenish-black		
*Hardness	3.5 – 4		
Cleavage	poor		
*Fracture	conchoidal to uneven; brittle		
Habit	crystals uncommon, usually massive and compact		
Twinning	frequent lamellar twinning	Examples	Rio Tinto (Spain), Savoy (France), Mansfeld (Germany), Sulitjelma (Norway), Cyprus, Mount Lyell (Tasmania), Ducktown, Tennessee (USA), Sudbury (Canada); also Chile, USSR, Zaire and Zambia
Specific gravity	4.1 – 4.3		
Other tests	soluble in nitric acid; burns in flame, colouring it green and giving off toxic, irritating fumes		
Crystal system	tetragonal		
Alteration	to sulphates, malachite, azurite and limonite on		

Cu_5FeS_4 Bornite

Bornite, which is also known as Erubescite or Peacock ore, is characterized by its iridescent tarnish and the red colour of fresh surfaces. It will eventually turn black after prolonged exposure. It was called 'horse-flesh ore' in Cornwall, England, where it was once mined. Bornite is a common ore of copper, found in high-temperature veins, intrusive igneous rocks, pegmatites and contact metamorphic rocks. It is often associated with the minerals chalcopyrite and chalcocite. It was named after Ignatius von Born, a distinguished eighteenth-century mineralogist.

Massive form

fresh surface

Massive form

iridescent surface

Bornite

	BORNITE		
*Colour	coppery red or bronze, rapidly tarnishes on exposure to become iridescent, with a purple and blue film	**Other tests**	soluble in nitric acid, leaving a deposit of sulphur; fuses fairly easily, giving a magnetic globule
Lustre	metallic	**Crystal system**	tetragonal (pseudo-cubic)
Transparency	opaque	**Alteration**	alters to chalcocite, malachite, azurite
Streak	pale grey-black, slightly shining	**Occurrence**	in pegmatites or hydrothermal veins; a common primary ore mineral of mixed sulphide veins; the dominant constituent of the copper deposits in the shales of the Kupferschiefer of Mansfeld (Germany)
*Hardness	3		
Cleavage	poor		
Fracture	subconchoidal or uneven; brittle		
Habit	commonly as compact granular masses, or crystalline as cubes, dodecahedra or octahedra	**Examples**	Cornwall (England), Tsumeb (Namibia), Butte, Montana (USA), Mount Lyell (Tasmania)
Twinning	on octahedron		
Specific gravity	4.9–5.4		

Chalcocite Cu_2S

Chalcocite (also called chalcosine or copper glance) is a valuable ore of copper. It commonly occurs in sulphide deposits where percolating water dissolves copper minerals near the surface and redeposits them below the water table. In this zone of secondary enrichment it is associated with bornite. In the weathered zone above, it is associated with azurite, cuprite and malachite. Chalcocite is an important 'porphyry copper' deposit. It also forms as a secondary deposit through the alteration of chalcopyrite. It forms attractive pseudo-hexagonal crystals in Cornwall, England, the Transvaal, South Africa and Bristol, Connecticut, USA. It is named after the Greek *chalkos*, meaning 'copper'.

Chalcocite in copper ore

Chalcocite crystals

Pseudohexagonal crystals

	CHALCOCITE		
*Colour	black or lead-grey, often with greenish or bluish tarnish	Crystal system	orthorhombic
Lustre	metallic	Alteration	to malachite, azurite, covellite
Transparency	opaque	Occurrence	in veins of hydrothermal sulphide deposits; may be associated with other copper minerals, e.g. cuprite, malachite, azurite
Streak	black, may shine		
Hardness	2.5–3		
Cleavage	poor, parallel to prism faces		
Fracture	conchoidal; brittle, sectile, almost malleable		
Habit	usually massive with a compact or granular structure; rarely as prismatic crystals	Examples	Cornwall (England), Kongsberg (Norway), Monte Catini (Italy), Tsumeb (Namibia), Butte, Montana (USA)
Twinning	often gives stellate groups of three individuals		
Specific gravity	5.5–5.8		
Other tests	soluble in hot nitric acid, leaving a sulphur precipitate; colours a flame green, giving off fumes of sulphur dioxide		

PbS Galena

Galena, the main ore of lead, is one of the most abundant and widely distributed sulphides. Because it almost always contains silver – up to 1 per cent – galena may also form an important source of silver. Galena is often found in hydrothermal veins, in association with chalcopyrite, pyrite and sphalerite, and also with the gangue minerals baryte, calcite, dolomite, fluorite and quartz. In higher temperature veins, associated minerals may be garnet, diopside and feldspar. Enormous deposits occur (with sphalerite) in the limestones and cherts of the Tri-State mining district of Missouri, Oklahoma and Kansas. The name is derived from the Greek for 'lead ore'. The most important use of lead is for making storage batteries, pipes and shot.

Cubic and octohedral crystals

brown surface alteration

Crystals

Crystals with gangue minerals

Cubic crystals

	GALENA
*Colour	lead-grey, cleavage surfaces may blacken with time
*Lustre	metallic, tarnishing dull
Transparency	opaque
Streak	lead-grey
Hardness	2.5
*Cleavage	perfect cubic, often breaking into smaller cubes when hit
Fracture	flat, even or conchoidal; brittle
*Habit	cubes, rarely octahedra; often massive, and coarsely or finely granular
Twinning	common, penetration or contact twins on octahedron
*Specific gravity	7.4 – 7.6
Other tests	soluble when heated in hydrochloric acid, giving off hydrogen sulphide with its characteristic smell of bad eggs; dissolves in nitric acid to produce small flakes of sulphur and a fine white precipitate
Crystal system	cubic
Occurrence	a hydrothermal mineral of medium-temperature deposits, often with sphalerite; also found in sedimentary rocks through the replacement of pre-existing rock by circulating waters
Examples	Cumberland (England), Broken Hill (Australia), Leadville, Colorado and Magdalena Mines, New Mexico (USA), Santa Eulalia (Mexico), Germany

Cinnabar *HgS*

The poisonous mineral cinnabar is the most important ore of mercury, but is found in large quantities at few localities. The Chinese and others used it as the pigment vermilion. Native mercury, the only mineral which is liquid at room temperature, is occasionally found in cinnabar deposits. Mercury is used in the production of chemicals and paints and in thermometers and other instruments. The most important cinnabar deposits occur as masses and impregnations in lavas, cavernous limestones, and clays, in such places as Almadén, Spain, Idria, Yugoslavia and Monte Amiata, Italy. Minerals found in association with cinnabar are baryte, calcite, chalcedony, pyrite, quartz, realgar and stibnite. The name cinnabar is thought to have originated in India, where it is applied to a red resin.

Adamantine crystals

Massive form

Tabular crystal

	CINNABAR		
*Colour	scarlet, cochineal-red or brownish red		heated in a tube
Lustre	adamantine when crystalline	**Crystal system**	trigonal
Transparency	transparent to translucent, or opaque when dull or earthy	**Occurrence**	found in a wide variety of rocks, often associated with volcanic activity, such as hot springs; also as low-temperature hydrothermal veins, and as replacement deposits in sedimentary rocks associated with igneous activity; may be found as alluvial deposits following erosion of older rocks
*Streak	bright scarlet		
Hardness	2–2.5		
*Cleavage	perfect prismatic		
Fracture	subconchoidal or uneven; somewhat sectile		
Habit	rarely crystalline, as rhombohedra or as thick tabular crystals, also prismatic; earthy films, granular or massive		
Twinning	common, basal	**Examples**	Almadén (Spain), Idria (Yugoslavia), Monte Amiata (Italy), New Almaden (USA), Nikotowa (USSR), Hunan Province (China), the Altai Mountains (Outer Mongolia)
*Specific gravity	8–8.2		
Other tests	insoluble in acids; mercury droplets form on wall when		

ZnS Sphalerite

The term sphalerite comes from the Greek *sphaleros*, meaning treacherous. This is because it has often been confused with galena, although it contains no lead. Similarly, it is also called zincblende or blende, from a German word meaning blind or deceiving. It is an important and common ore of zinc, often found with galena. By-products of sphalerite-working usually include cadmium, gallium and indium. Zinc is used as sheet zinc and for galvanizing iron. It is also a component of brass. Most sphalerite contains some iron, which affects its colour. Pure varieties are yellow or reddish-brown, but if the mineral contains more than 10 per cent iron, it appears black and is called *marmatite*.

Adamantine crystals

Adamantine crystals

Tetrahedral crystal

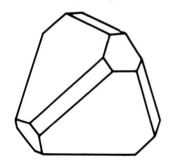

	SPHALERITE		
*Colour	commonly black or brown, sometimes yellow or white, rarely colourless		under ultraviolet light; soluble in hydrochloric acid, giving off hydrogen sulphide
*Lustre	adamantine or resinous	**Crystal system**	cubic
Transparency	transparent, translucent or opaque	**Alteration**	to limonite, hemimorphite or smithsonite
Streak	light yellow to brownish, or white	**Occurrence**	in hydrothermal vein deposits associated with galena, argentite, baryte, chalcopyrite and fluorite; in low- and high-temperature replacement deposits (skarns); in metamorphic rocks
Hardness	3.5 – 4		
*Cleavage	perfect, parallel to dodecahedron		
Fracture	conchoidal; brittle		
Habit	tetrahedra and dodecahedra common; also massive and compact, botryoidal or fibrous		
Twinning	common on octahedron	**Examples**	Kapnik (Hungary), Trepca (Yugoslavia), Alston Moor (England), Santander (Spain), Tri-State (USA), Sullivan (Canada), Broken Hill (Australia)
Specific gravity	3.9 – 4.2		
Other tests	pale varieties may fluoresce		

Molybdenite MoS_2

Molybdenite, the main ore of molybdenum, occurs widely, but in small deposits. The term was first used for lead-bearing substances, and later its meaning was extended to include graphite and molybdenite. These two minerals are similar, but molybdenite has a higher specific gravity, a lighter bluish tinge and a brighter metallic lustre. It often occurs as scaly masses and the individual layers are easily bent. Molybdenite is used as a dry lubricant, which is resistant to high temperatures. Molybdenum is used to make hard, resistant steels, and also in the manufacture of tools, drills and electrical equipment.

Six-sided tabular crystals

Molybdenite in granitic rock

Molybdenite with quartz and molybdite

MOLYBDENITE	
*Colour	bluish grey
Lustre	metallic
Transparency	opaque
Streak	lead-grey, greenish tint distinguishes it from graphite
*Hardness	1–1.5
Cleavage	perfect parallel to base; laminae are flexible but not elastic
*Tenacity	sectile and almost malleable
Habit	tabular crystals have a hexagonal outline; usually as leafy or scaly masses, also massive or sometimes granular
Specific gravity	4.7–4.8
*Other tests	greasy feel; leaves a bluish-grey mark on paper
Crystal system	hexagonal

Occurrence usually found in granites, or sometimes diorites, in cavities, pegmatites or high-temperature pneumatolytic veins, associated with cassiterite, fluorite, scheelite and wolframite. Also of contact metamorphic origin occurring with garnet, pyroxenes, scheelite, pyrite and tourmaline

Examples disseminated in quartz veins crossing granite at Climax, Colorado (USA); good crystals in Edison, New Jersey (USA); also in Australia, Bolivia, Italy and Norway

Sb_2S_3 Stibnite

Stibnite, also known as antimonite, is the chief source of commercial antimony. It is widely distributed, but does not usually occur in large deposits. Stibnite is found mostly in low temperature hydrothermal veins, but also occurs as a replacement deposit and as a hot spring deposit. It may be associated with a variety of other minerals such as realgar, orpiment, galena, marcasite, pyrite, cinnabar and quartz. The largest deposits are in the Hunan Province of China, where stibnite occurs as veins and pockets in brecciated sandstone. The name is derived from the old Greek word for the mineral, *stibi*, meaning 'antimony'.

Acicular crystals

Prismatic crystals

Stibnite

STIBNITE		
*Colour	steel-grey	
*Lustre	metallic, may tarnish, sometimes iridescent on surface	
Transparency	opaque	
Streak	steel-grey	
*Hardness	2	
*Cleavage	perfect lengthwise cleavage	
Fracture	subconchoidal; sectile, brittle but thin laminae slightly flexible	
*Habit	elongated prismatic or needle-like crystals, striated along length, may be bent or twisted; commonly radiating; sometimes granular	
Specific gravity	4.5 – 4.6	
Other tests	thin splinters melt in a flame colouring it greenish blue; powder soluble in concentrated hydrochloric acid; decomposes easily in potassium hydroxide solution staining it orange	
Crystal system	orthorhombic	
Alteration	alters to antimony oxides, e.g. red needle-like kermesite crystals or other yellow powdery minerals called antimony ochres	
Occurrence	in veins associated with silver, lead and mercury minerals; also as a hot spring deposit with realgar, orpiment and cinnabar	
Examples	Hunan province (China), Island of Shikoku (Japan), Romania, Bolivia and Mexico	

Rutile TiO_2

Rutile, an ore of titanium, is a high-temperature form of titanium dioxide. Low-temperature forms are *anatase* and *brookite*. Rutile is a primary mineral in igneous rocks and high-temperature metamorphic rocks. Because of its resistance to alteration, it occurs in placer deposits. Sands rich in rutile are worked in Australia. A well-known rutile-bearing granite occurs in Kragero, Norway. It is collected for its attractive twins and multiple intergrowths, though gem-quality crystals, found at Minas Gerais, Brazil, are extremely rare. Needle-like inclusions in rock-crystal (quartz), known as *sagenite* or *needle-stone*, make attractive polished specimens. Rutile disperses light six times as much as diamond; such 'fire' makes it easily detected. It is named from the Latin for 'golden red'.

Needles in quartz

Red adamantine crystals

Knee-shaped twin crystal

	RUTILE		
*Colour	reddish brown, sometimes yellow or black	**Occurrence**	accessory mineral in many plutonic igneous rocks, also eclogites; in some pegmatites, apatite and quartz veins; common accessory in gneisses and schists; in sands, clays and shales as a detrital mineral
*Lustre	adamantine, high dispersion can give 'fire'		
Transparency	transparent when thin, most often translucent, occasionally opaque		
Streak	pale brown	**Examples**	in fissures in the Swiss Alps; Graves Mountain, Georgia and Nelson County, Virginia (USA). Sites in Australia, Brazil, Italy, Mexico and Norway
Hardness	6–6.5		
Cleavage	prismatic, distinct		
Fracture	conchoidal to uneven		
*Habit	commonly needle-like, vertically striated crystals; sometimes granular, massive		
*Twinning	common, often giving knee-shaped twins (see also cassiterite)		
Specific gravity	4.2–4.3		
Crystal system	tetragonal		

SnO_2 Cassiterite

Cassiterite or tinstone is the only abundant tin ore. The deposits in Cornwall, England, were the main source until the nineteenth century. It is one of the few minerals that does not occur in great quantities in the United States. A concentrically banded form with a fibrous structure is called *wood tin*, or *toad's eye* when formed on a small scale. Some gem-quality cassiterite occurs, especially in Spain and Namibia, but most is collected for the knee-shaped twins that are common. Cassiterite has an unusually high specific gravity for a non-metallic mineral. This property, together with its high resistance to weathering, mean that cassiterite is often found in stream and beach deposits. The name is derived from the Greek word for 'tin'. The main uses for tin are in the metal-plating industry and in various alloys.

Crystals

Crystals

Pyramidal crystal

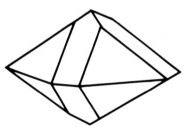

	CASSITERITE	Crystal system	tetragonal
Colour	reddish brown to brownish black	**Occurrence**	in high-temperature hydrothermal veins with quartz within and near to granites; the associated granite may be altered to a quartz-muscovite rock called greisen; associated minerals include mica, quartz, fluorite, wolframite, arsenopyrite, native bismuth, topaz and tourmaline; rounded pebbles are called stream tin
*Lustre	adamantine to submetallic, splendent		
Transparency	translucent		
*Streak	grey-white to brownish		
Hardness	6–7		
Cleavage	prismatic, imperfect		
Fracture	subconchoidal to uneven; brittle		
*Habit	short prismatic crystals, sometimes long with steep pyramidal ends; radially fibrous, concretionary masses (wood tin)	**Examples**	ore deposits in Malaysia, Sumatra (Indonesia), Yunnan (China), USSR and Bolivia; good crystals in Cornwall (England) and Erzgebirge (Germany)
*Twinning	common, to give well-known 'knee-twins' (see also rutile)		
*Specific gravity	6.8–7.1 (to 6.1 for fibrous masses)		

Cuprite Cu_2O

Cuprite, also known as red copper oxide, is an important copper ore, which occurs in large amounts as a secondary mineral in copper deposits. It resembles cinnabar and hematite in colour, but it can be distinguished by its hardness, which is between the two, and its streak. The fine, hair-like crystal form is called *chalcotrichite*. An earthy, reddish brown variety containing iron oxides is called the tile ore. Gem-quality cuprite, called *ruby copper*, is rare. The only sites containing stones suitable for cutting are Santa Rita, New Mexico, USA, and Onganyo, Namibia. The name is derived from the Latin *cuprum* meaning 'copper'.

Cuprite

Red, matted, acicular crystals

Crystals on calcite

CUPRITE	
*Colour	red to very dark red
Lustre	submetallic to adamantine, or earthy
Transparency	subtranslucent, subtransparent when thin
*Streak	brownish red, shining
*Hardness	3.5 – 4
Cleavage	poor
Fracture	uneven, conchoidal; brittle
Habit	octahedral crystals, more rarely dodecahedra or cubes; sometimes in matted, straight hair-like crystals; massive or earthy
Specific gravity	5.8 – 6.1
Crystal system	cubic
Alteration	to malachite
Occurrence	common in the oxidized zone of copper deposits

often accompanied by malachite, azurite, chalcocite and native copper

Examples Redruth, Liskeard and the Lizard, Cornwall (England), Chessy near Lyon (France), Broken Hill, NSW (Australia), Bisbee, Arizona (USA), Tsumeb (Namibia)

Fe_3O_4 **Magnetite**

Magnetite has a strongly magnetic character. People of early civilizations noticed that magnetized specimens, called *lodestones*, attracted other magnetic materials and, after swinging freely, aligned themselves in the Earth's magnetic field. Lodestone is found in Magnet Cove, Arkansas, USA. Magnetite grains can occur in detrital sediments, associated with corundum deposits. The magnetite can be extracted with a magnet. Magnetite is an important iron ore. Swedish magnetite, which is associated with iron silicates, produces an extremely hard steel.

Massive form

Octahedral crystals

Lodestone attracting iron nail

	MAGNETITE	
*Colour	black	
Lustre	metallic or submetallic to dull	
Transparency	opaque	
*Streak	black	
Hardness	5.5–6.5	
Cleavage	none, octahedral parting	
Fracture	subconchoidal	
Habit	octahedral crystals, less commonly dodecahedra; granular or massive	
Twinning	common	
Specific gravity	5.2	
*Other tests	strongly magnetic	
Crystal system	cubic	
Occurrence	common; accessory in igneous rocks, sometimes accumulating in concentrations high enough to be of economic value; in metamorphic rocks and high-temperature mineral veins; in detrital sediments and in iron-formations	
Examples	large deposits are found in Scandinavia (e.g. Kiruna, Sweden), Bushveld (South Africa), Adirondacks New York (USA) and the Ural Mountains (USSR); black sands are widespread in Alaska, California, Idaho, Montana, Colorado, Oregon and Washington (USA); beautiful crystals are found at Bolzano (Italy) and in Binnenthal (Switzerland)	

Hematite Fe_2O_3

Hematite is named after the Greek word for blood. When earthy and mixed with clay minerals, it forms red ochre, which has long been used as a pigment. It is the leading iron ore, because it is both common and rich in iron. Varieties are *specularite* (a crystalline form with a bright metallic lustre), *kidney ore* (reniform masses), and *micaceous hematite* or *iron mica* (small shiny masses). Distinguishing features of hematite are the colour of its streak and its hardness, which makes it a useful polishing material, called *jeweller's rouge*. In ancient times hematite was used to stop bleeding, acting in a similar way to alum, which is used in styptic pencils. It is the most oxidized form of iron oxide and is a major constituent of rust.

weathered surface coating

Botryoidal form

Botryoidal form

Specular hematite

tabular crystals

metallic lustre

	HEMATITE	**Twinning**	common, to give striations
*Colour	steel-grey to iron-black, sometimes iridescent; dull to bright red when massive or earthy	**Specific gravity**	4.9 – 5.3
		Crystal system	trigonal
Lustre	metallic, or dull and earthy	**Occurrence**	widely distributed; accessory mineral in igneous rocks, and in hydrothermal veins; formed under sedimentary conditions often as ooliths or as a cement, as a primary mineral; also as a secondary mineral on the weathering of iron-bearing minerals
Transparency	opaque, translucent in thin pieces		
*Streak	dark red to red-brown		
*Hardness	5 – 6		
Cleavage	none		
Fracture	uneven; brittle		
Habit	crystals tabular or rhombohedral, sometimes with curved or striated faces; sometimes arranged in rose-like form in 'iron roses'; massive, laminated or earthy, often mammilated or botryoidal	**Examples**	Precambrian terrains in Lake Superior (USA), Brazil and Australia, Clinton Formation of New York, Pennsylvania and Alabama (USA), Lake District (England); iron roses in St. Gotthard (Switzerland) and Minas Gerais (Brazil)

Chromite always contains small quantities of magnesiochromite ($MgCr_2O_4$), spinel ($MgAl_2O_4$), and other spinels. Hence, the specific gravity of specimens varies considerably. Chromite is the only chromium ore. It is important in making steel alloys (especially stainless steel), chromium-plating, leather-tanning and paints. It is extremely resistant to high temperatures and is used to make bricks for lining blast furnaces. These bricks are usually made of crude chromite and coal tar. The brown streak and weaker magnetic character distinguish chromite from magnetite. Other useful distinguishing features are its insolubility in acids and its association with ultrabasic igneous rocks.

Massive form

Granular form

Aggregate of crystals

	CHROMITE
*Colour	black to brownish black
Lustre	metallic to submetallic
Transparency	opaque, translucent in thin flakes
*Streak	dark brown
Hardness	5.5
Cleavage	none
Fracture	uneven; brittle
Habit	rarely octahedral crystals; commonly massive, granular
Specific gravity	4.1–5.1
*Other tests	weakly magnetic
Crystal system	cubic
Occurrence	accessory mineral in ultrabasic igneous rocks and serpentinites derived from them; may be concentrated into workable layers in such rocks; sometimes in alluvial sands and gravels
Examples	important countries for production are South Africa, USSR, Albania and Zimbabwe; also found in the Stilwater Complex, Montana (USA); good crystals occur in Namibia

Corundum Al_2O_3

The best known and prized varieties of this hard and durable mineral are *rubies* (red) and *sapphires* (blue). Yellow, green, and brown forms also occur. 'Star' sapphires and rubies are opalescent and display six- or three-pointed stars in reflected light, an effect called *asterism*, caused by minute rutile crystals. The price of high-quality gemstones can exceed that of diamonds. The presence of corundum in alluvial sands and gravels is due to the mineral's extreme hardness, which is second only to diamond, and durability. An impure form of corundum, called *emery*, is used as an abrasive.

Ruby

Blue, barrel-shaped crystal in gneiss

Corundum

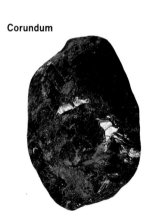

	CORUNDUM		
Colour	very variable; can be blue, red, yellow, brown, green	**Occurrence**	accessory mineral in syenites and nepheline syenites; in contact metamorphosed shales and bauxite; in some feldspar pegmatites; in metamorphosed impure limestones; in river and placer deposits
Lustre	adamantine to vitreous		
Transparency	transparent to translucent		
Streak	white		
*Hardness	9		
Cleavage	none, basal parting		
Fracture	uneven to conchoidal	**Examples**	Mogok (Myanmar, formerly Burma), Sri Lanka, Madagascar, South Africa, Glebe Hill, Ardnamurchan (Scotland), Naxos Island (Greece), Turkey and the central Urals (USSR)
*Habit	rough prisms or barrel-shaped crystals bounded by steep pyramids; faces show horizontal ridges and striations; also massive and granular, called emery (often with magnetite and spinel)		
Twinning	common, often repeated, giving striations		
*Specific gravity	4		
Crystal system	trigonal		

Spinel is not a single mineral, but it is used as the name for a series of minerals that contain varying amounts of magnesian spinel with iron, zinc and manganese, namely *hercynite* ($FeAl_2O_4$), *gahnite* ($ZnAl_2O_4$), and *galaxite* ($MnAl_2O_4$). Chromite may also be present. Gem-quality stones have long been prized, especially the red ruby spinel. Often mistaken for rubies and sapphires, spinel was collected in royal treasuries. The best known stone is the Timur Ruby in the British Crown Jewels. Many spinels, like corundum, are now manufactured synthetically in large quantities. Red spinel turns brown or black on heating, changing to green, colourless and back to red on cooling.

Ruby spinel

Ruby spinel

Single crystal

Blue-black form, with calcite and quartz

	SPINEL
Colour	variable; colourless when pure, often red, but also blue, green, brown or black
Lustre	vitreous
Transparency	transparent to almost opaque
Streak	white or grey to brown
Hardness	7.5 – 8
Cleavage	none; octahedral parting
Fracture	conchoidal
*Habit	octahedral crystals, massive
*Twinning	common on octahedron ('spinel twins')
Specific gravity	3.5 – 4.1
Crystal system	cubic
Occurrence	accessory in igneous rocks (e.g. gabbro); in magnesium- and aluminium-rich contact metamorphosed dolomitic limestones and aluminous xenoliths in igneous rocks; in gravels due to its resistance to weathering and hardness
Examples	gem quality in Myanmar (formerly Burma), Sri Lanka and India, also Thailand, Madagascar and Afghanistan; good specimens at Monte Somma, Vesuvius (Italy), Orange County, New York and Sterling Hill Mine, Ogdensburg, New York (USA)

Pyrolusite MnO_2

Pyrolusite is an important ore of the metal manganese, which is used in steel-making, both to remove oxygen and sulphur, and as an alloying metal. Rare, well-formed crystals are called *polianite*. The massive form is by far the most abundant, the colour and the softness being the main diagnostic feature. The name comes from the Greek words meaning 'fire' and 'wash', referring to the fact that pyrolusite was once used to remove iron oxide discoloration in glass-making. Pyrolusite occurs as a constituent of the mixture of black hydrous manganese-bearing minerals known as *wad*, together with psilomelane and manganite.

Radiating habit

Dendritic form

Crystals

	PYROLUSITE
*Colour	black or blue-black
Lustre	metallic to dull and earthy
Transparency	opaque
Streak	black to blue-black
Hardness	6–6.5 (1–2 when massive)
Cleavage	perfect, prismatic
Fracture	uneven; splintery
Habit	usually massive, often reniform, concretionary or powdery; forms dendritic (plant-like) markings on joint surfaces; crystals rare, well-formed prisms
Specific gravity	5.1 (crystals), 4.4–5 (massive)
Crystal system	tetragonal
Occurrence	in oxidized zone of manganese ore deposits, in bog or shallow water sediments, as nodules on the sea-bed and in quartz veins
Examples	found at Platten, Bavaria, (Germany), Czechoslovakia, Cornwall (England). Large deposits at Nikepol (Ukraine), Chiatura, Georgia (USSR), Deccan (India), Brazil, Cuba, Ghana, South Africa

oethite forms attractive but rare
rystals. Common forms are massive,
ith a radially fibrous structure. It is
ound in large amounts as the
morphous mineral assemblage called
monite. Limonite is a blanket term for
ll forms of hydrated ferric oxide, which
as been formed by the oxidation and
eathering of iron minerals. It includes
he famous yellow ochres associated
ith iron deposits and used as pigments.
imonite is distinguished from
rystalline goethite by its vitreous
ustre and lack of cleavage. Both have a
haracteristic yellow-brown streak.
oethite is deposited as a sediment in
ogs at high altitudes, where it forms
og-iron ores. It is named after the
erman poet J.W. von Goethe, who
ollected minerals.

**Iridescent
stalactites**

Limonite nodule

Goethite

	GOETHITE
Colour	dark brown, but yellow when as fine-grained earthy varieties
Lustre	adamantine when crystalline, often silky when massive
Transparency	thin fragments transparent, opaque when massive
***Streak**	yellow-brown
Hardness	5–5.5
Cleavage	one perfect
Fracture	uneven
Habit	crystals prismatic or scaly, but rare; usually massive with a radially fibrous structure as concretions, stalactites or botryoidal forms
Specific gravity	3.3 (massive) – 4.3 (crystals)
Crystal system	orthorhombic
Occurrence	widespread in limonite in weathered or hydrothermally altered iron-bearing rocks; as sediments in bogs at high latitudes and rarely precipitated in marine conditions; it occurs at the outcrop of sulphide deposits
Examples	large deposits in Alsace-Lorraine (France), Labrador (Canada), Westphalia (Germany) and Cuba; crystals at Lostwithiel and Botallach, Cornwall (England), Pribram (Czechoslovakia), Lake Onega (USSR) and Pikes Peak, Colorado (USA)

Ilmenite $FeTiO_3$

Ilmenite, an ore of titanium, is a black mineral with a metallic lustre when pure. It can contain varying amounts of the related magnesian mineral *giekielite* ($MgTiO_3$), which affects its physical properties. The variety *menaccanite*, found at Menaccan Sands, Cornwall, England, was one of the first reported descriptions of ilmenite. The occurrence of ilmenite in sands reflects its high resistance to weathering. In magmas, it is prone to segregate with magnetite or hematite, because of its relatively high specific gravity. It is distinguished from hematite by its streak, and from magnetite by its non-magnetic nature.

Ilmenite with feldspar

Tabular crystals

Single crystal

metallic lustr

	ILMENITE	
Colour	black, described as iron black	
Lustre	metallic to submetallic	
Transparency	opaque	
*Streak	black to brownish black	
Hardness	5–6	
Cleavage	none, basal partings	
Fracture	conchoidal	
Habit	thick tabular crystals; massive, compact; disseminated grains in basic igneous rocks	
Twinning	common	
Specific gravity	4.5–5	
*Other tests	non-magnetic	
Crystal system	trigonal	
Occurrence	common accessory as grains in basic igneous rocks, such as gabbros and diorites; larger amounts as ilmenite-magnetite or ilmenite-hematite segregations in gabbros and anorthosites; it is concentrated in some beach sands, alongside magnetite, rutile and monazite; less commonly in quartz veins and pegmatites	
Examples	Egersund (southern Norway), Taberg (Sweden), Alland Lake, Quebec (Canada) and Adirondacks, New York (USA). Other large deposits in India, Brazil and USSR. Beach placer deposits at Travancore (India). Large crystals at Kragero (Norway)	

Halite, or rock salt, is best known as common table salt. It occurs within thick, stratified evaporite deposits and in domes. These deposits form when layers of light, plastic halite are compressed and rise up through overlying layers of sediment. Halite is formed where enclosed bodies of seawater evaporate, and the different salts separate out in layers, as in the Permian evaporites of Stassfurt, Germany. Apart from its use in the preparation of food, halite is the main source of chlorine used in the manufacture of household bleach. By-products include potassium, magnesium, bromine and iodine.

cubic cleavage

White cubic crystals

Cubic crystals

Granular form

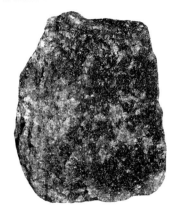

	HALITE	**Crystal system**	cubic
Colour	colourless or white when pure, often yellow or red, sometimes with blue or purple tints	**Occurrence**	as a precipitate in sedimentary deposits, sometimes interbedded with clay, and characteristically associated with other evaporites (sylvite, gypsum and anhydrite) and with dolomite; also as a direct sublimate from volcanic exhalations
Lustre	vitreous		
Transparency	transparent to translucent		
Streak	white		
Hardness	2–2.5		
Cleavage	perfect cubic		
Fracture	conchoidal; brittle		
Habit	often as masses of interlocking cubic crystals, occasionally as octahedra; cubes with hollow faces are known as hopper crystals; also massive and granular	**Examples**	Cheshire (England), Lorraine (France), Salzburg (Austria), New York, Michigan and Ohio (USA)
Specific gravity	2.2		
*Other tests	salty, soluble in water; colours a flame bright yellow		

Fluorite CaF_2

The best known type of fluorite is *Blue John*, a violet-blue and white or yellowish banded variety used in jewellery and vases. Miners once called the beautifully coloured crystals 'ore flowers'. It is a widely distributed mineral and is now mined in vast quantities. It is an important raw material used to prepare several fluorine compounds, such as hydrofluoric acid. It is also used in the manufacture of pottery, in the optical and plastics industries, and in the metallurgical treatment of bauxite. Lower grade fluorite is used as a flux in steel-making and foundry work. Its name comes from the Latin *fluere*, meaning 'to flow', which refers to its use as a flux. It is also known as fluorspar.

Blue John

Radiating crystals

Cubic crystals with bands of colour

Octahedron

	FLUORITE		
Colour	variable; colourless when pure, tinted by impurities to blue, pink, purple, green or yellow		under ultraviolet light; when heated to temperatures above 100°C (212°F), emits light in darkness, i.e., it thermoluminesces
*Lustre	vitreous	**Crystal system**	cubic
Transparency	transparent to translucent	**Occurrence**	found in sulphide deposits as gangue with barytes and quartz; sometimes found in pegmatites; can also form from saline waters in enclosed basins
Streak	white		
Hardness	4		
*Cleavage	parallel to octahedron		
Fracture	conchoidal to uneven; brittle		
Habit	crystals common, as cubes or octahedra; compact, or coarsely or finely granular		
Twinning	interpenetrant twins typical	**Examples**	Cumberland and Derbyshire (England), Bolzano (Italy), St. Gotthard (Switzerland), Kongsberg (Norway), Bancroft (Canada), Jefferson County, New York (USA), Kazakhstan (USSR)
Specific gravity	3–3.3		
Other tests	soluble in concentrated sulphuric acid, giving off fumes of hydrofluoric acid; often strongly fluorescent		

KCl **Sylvite**

Sylvite, or sylvine, is often associated with halite, but is much less common, because the potassium ions are retained by clay minerals rather than being dissolved in water. Sylvite also resembles halite, but it is less dense, has a more bitter taste, and is less brittle, deforming readily under pressure. It may be reddish because of disseminated hematite, or purple due to exposure to natural radiation. It is used as a fertilizer, either directly or in the preparation of potassium salts. The deposits at Saskatchewan, Canada are over 900m (2950ft) deep and form the world's most important resources. The name sylvite comes from the early chemical name for the salt _sal digestiva sylvii_, after the German anatomist Franciscus Sylvius.

Cupriferous form

Sylvite

Crystals on halite

	SYLVITE		
Colour	colourless or white, bluish or yellowish red	**Occurrence**	associated with halite and carnallite, occurring as a saline residue in Stassfurt (Germany) and other salt deposits; also around fumaroles of volcanoes, e.g. Vesuvius (Italy)
Lustre	vitreous		
Transparency	transparent when pure		
Streak	white		
Hardness	2		
Cleavage	perfect cubic	**Examples**	Stassfurt (Germany), Etna and Vesuvius (Italy), Kalusz (Poland), Saskatchewan (Canada), Utah, Texas and New Mexico (USA)
Fracture	uneven; less brittle than halite		
Habit	rare cubic crystals, modified by octahedron; more commonly granular crystalline masses		
Specific gravity	2		
*Other tests	salty, more bitter than halite; soluble in water; colours a flame purplish red; not as deliquescent as halite		
Crystal system	cubic		

Calcite $CaCO_3$

Calcite is a major rock-forming mineral. It is the principal component of limestones, other calcareous sedimentary rocks and marble. The calcite in limestones may originate as an accumulation of shells or as a precipitate. Other calcite precipitates are travertine and tufa – the former in stalactites and stalagmites. It is also a common gangue mineral in hydrothermal veins. The large clear crystals of the variety *Iceland spar* display double refraction – that is, when placed on a sheet of paper marked with a spot, two spots are seen, and, on revolving the crystal, one spot remains still, while the other appears to revolve around it. Limestones are quarried to produce lime for cement. This process is energy-intensive, because the rock has to be heated to high temperatures in order to decompose calcite into carbon dioxide (CO_2) and lime (CaO).

Nail-head spar

Barrel-shaped crystals

Stalactitic form

	CALCITE		
Colour	usually colourless or white, may be brown, red, blue, green or black		fibrous, granular, massive or stalactitic
		Twinning	common
Lustre	vitreous, somewhat pearly on cleavages	**Specific gravity**	2.7
		Other tests	effervesces readily and dissolves in cold, dilute hydrochloric acid
Transparency	transparent to translucent, almost opaque when deeply coloured	**Crystal system**	trigonal
		Occurrence	a widespread rock-forming mineral; in sedimentary rocks, such as limestones, and in metamorphic rocks, such as marble
Streak	white		
Hardness	3		
*Cleavage	rhombohedral, perfect		
Fracture	conchoidal, but rare due to perfect cleavage		
Habit	very variable; commonly flat rhombohedra; prisms topped with rhombohedra form nail-head spar; steep scalenohedra form dog-tooth spar; aggregates are	**Examples**	large clear prisms of Iceland Spar (Iceland), the Harz Mountains (Germany), Colorado (USA); dog-tooth spar in Cumberland (England)

$_{CaCO_3}$ Aragonite

Aragonite is a polymorph of the more common calcite. (Polymorphs are substances with the same chemical composition, but with different properties.) Aragonite is unstable when exposed to high temperatures and pressures. As a result, fossil mollusc shells originally made of aragonite are now of calcite. Although unstable, aragonite can be produced by biological action or by precipitation under the right conditions of temperature, or in the presence of dissolved metals, such as lead, strontium or zinc. It is distinguished from calcite by its fibrous, rounded form, its lack of distinct rhombohedral cleavage, and a higher specific gravity. Aragonite is used as an ornamental stone. A popular banded variety is called *onyx* or *onyx marble*. *Flos-ferri* consists of slender, intertwined branches.

Acicular crystals

Pseudohexagonal twinned crystals

Flos-ferri

	ARAGONITE	Crystal system	orthorhombic
Colour	colourless to white, or yellowish	**Occurrence**	less widespread than calcite; deposited from hot springs or in caves; in veins or cavities with calcite and dolomite; as the nacreous shell on many molluscs and in pearls
Lustre	vitreous		
Transparency	transparent to translucent		
Streak	white		
Hardness	3.5 – 4		
Cleavage	poor		
Fracture	subconchoidal	**Examples**	Molina de Aragon (Spain), Fort Collins, Colorado (USA), Bastennes (France), Alston Moor, Cumberland (England)
*Habit	stout, prismatic, twinned crystals with a pseudo-hexagonal symmetry are most common; untwinned crystals rare; stalactitic and encrusting masses with a fibrous structure		
Twinning	very common		
Specific gravity	2.9		
*Other tests	soluble with effervescence in dilute hydrochloric acid		

Dolomite $CaMg(CO_3)_2$

Dolomite is similar to calcite and accompanies it in many limestones. It usually occurs as a secondary mineral, formed by the reaction of magnesium-bearing fluids seeping through limestones. The variety *pearl spar* is white, grey or pale brown, with a pearly lustre, while *brown*, *rhomb* or *bitter-spar* are iron-bearing varieties, coloured brown by the presence of *ankerite*, a cross between dolomite and siderite. The faces of dolomite crystals are often curved, sometimes so acutely that the crystals become saddle-shaped. Dolomitic rocks are useful building materials and refractories (materials that can withstand high temperatures). Dolomite, a source of magnesium and fluxes in the steel industry, is distinguished from calcite by its reluctance to dissolve in dilute acid.

overlapping scales

Aggregate of yellowish crystals

Saddle-shaped crystal

Aggregate of pink crystals

	DOLOMITE		
Colour	colourless, or white to cream and yellow brown; sometimes pale pink	**Crystal system**	trigonal
		Alteration	weathers brown
Lustre	vitreous	**Occurrence**	rock-forming mineral in dolomitic limestones, usually secondary; widespread gangue mineral in hydrothermal veins, especially accompanying galena and sphalerite
Transparency	translucent		
Streak	white		
Hardness	3.5−4		
Cleavage	rhombohedral, perfect		
Fracture	subconchoidal	**Examples**	Brosso and Traversella, Piedmont (Italy), Binnenthal (Switzerland), the Freiberg and Schneeberg Mines (Germany), Cornwall (England), Joplin, Missouri (USA)
Habit	rhombohedral crystals with curved faces, often composed of overlapping scales; massive, granular		
Twinning	common		
Specific gravity	2.8−2.9		
*Other tests	slowly dissolves with effervescence in cold, dilute hydrochloric acid, readily on warming		

$MgCO_3$ Magnesite

Unlike calcite and dolomite, magnesite does not usually form sedimentary rocks. Instead, it occurs as an alteration product of magnesian mineral-bearing rocks by water containing carbonic acid, or of carbonate-bearing rocks by water containing dissolved magnesium. Magnesite usually occurs as a replacement deposit in carbonaceous rocks. The white massive variety can have a porcelain-like appearance resembling chert due to the presence of opal. An important ore of magnesium, it is heated to drive off carbon dioxide leaving magnesium oxide (MgO), which is used in making refractory bricks and furnace linings, special cements, and in the paper industry. It has been used as an antacid for digestive disorders.

Magnesite

porcellaneous lustre

Massive, chalk-like form

Crystals

	MAGNESITE		
*Colour	white or colourless, often discoloured greyish or yellowish brown	Crystal system	trigonal
Lustre	vitreous, or dull when compact	Occurrence	uncommon; alteration product of peridotites alongside talc and serpentine; replacement mineral in dolomites and limestones
Transparency	transparent to translucent		
Streak	white		
Hardness	3.5–4.5		
*Cleavage	rhombohedral, perfect	Examples	Isle of Euboea and Macedonia (Greece), Styria (Austria), the Ural Mountains (USSR), Manchuria, Korea, Quebec (Canada), Paradise Mountains, Nevada (USA)
Fracture	conchoidal		
Habit	crystals rare and usually rhombohedral; massive, granular, fibrous or compact porcellaneous and chalk-like		
Specific gravity	3 (up to 3.2 with iron present)		
*Other tests	little reaction with cold dilute hydrochloric acid, dissolves with effervescence on warming		

Siderite FeCO₃

Siderite is a major source of iron for steel making, because it is easily worked, often free of sulphur and phosphorus, and sometimes manganese-rich. Its colour and higher specific gravity distinguish it from calcite and dolomite, and its rhombohedral cleavage, from sphalerite. It occurs in the Coal Measures as beds and nodules of impure iron carbonate called *clay ironstone*, which used to be a valuable iron ore. A dark carbonaceous variety is called *blackband*. *Oolitic ironstone* is formed most often by the same colloidal processes that form oolitic limestones. Less commonly, iron-rich fluids form siderite as a secondary mineral in calcareous rocks. When extensive, these deposits are economically important. Siderite is also known as chalybite, named after the *Chalybes*, ancient iron workers who lived by the Black Sea.

Aggregate of rhombohedral crystals

Single crystal

rhombohedral cleavage

Aggregate of crystals

pearly lustre

	SIDERITE
*Colour	brown, yellowish brown, grey-brown
Lustre	vitreous, inclining to pearly on cleavages
Transparency	transparent to translucent
Streak	white
Hardness	3.5 – 4.5
*Cleavage	rhombohedral, perfect
Fracture	uneven
*Habit	rhombohedral crystals often with curved faces made up of overlapping scales; massive, granular or concretionary
Twinning	common, often lamellar
*Specific gravity	4 (to 3.8 when magnesium is present)
*Other tests	dissolves slowly with effervescence in cold dilute hydrochloric acid, readily on warming
Crystal system	trigonal
Occurrence	widespread massive siderite deposits in sedimentary rocks, especially in clays and shales as concretions; gangue mineral in hydrothermal veins with pyrite and galena; as bog-iron ore in high latitude lakes and swamps
Examples	Mesozoic rocks in England, Belgium, Luxembourg and North France, especially in the Coal Measures of the English Midlands; large deposits in Pennsylvania (USA) and in veins in central Germany

$Cu_2CO_3(OH)_2$ **Malachite**

Malachite has long been prized as a semi-precious stone. Beautiful ornaments and table tops are made from banded forms of malachite. It was popular among the ancient Greeks and Romans, and it later became fashionable in the courts of the Russian Czars. Malachite is also a copper ore. One major deposit is at Shaba (formerly Katanga) province, Zaire. Crushed malachite has been used as a pigment. It is known as green copper carbonate, in contrast to azurite, known as blue copper carbonate. Malachite is named after the Greek for 'mallow', as it is similar in colour to a mallow leaf.

Crystals

Colour-banded form

Botryoidal form

MALACHITE	
*Colour	bright green
Lustre	fibrous aggregates silky to dull; crystals adamantine
Transparency	translucent
Streak	pale green
Hardness	3.5–4
Cleavage	perfect
Fracture	subconchoidal or uneven
*Habit	mammillated or botryoidal form with concentric bands and fibrous structure; crystals rare, tufts of twinned needles and prisms
Twinning	common
Specific gravity	3.9–4
*Other tests	soluble with effervescence in dilute hydrochloric acid
Crystal system	monoclinic
Occurrence	widespread in the oxidized zone of copper deposits as a secondary mineral, associated with azurite, cuprite, native copper, limonite and chrysocolla
Examples	large masses in the Shaba Province (Zaire); Demidoff Mine, Nizhne-Tagilisk and Sverdlovsk (Ural Mountains, USSR), for large masses; good crystals at Betzdorf (Germany), Chessy (France), Redruth, Cornwall (England) Copper Queen Mine, Bisbee, Arizona (USA)

Azurite $Cu_3(CO_3)(OH)_2$

Azurite is named after the Persian word for blue. Its attractive blue colour has made it a semi-precious stone, although its softness has limited its use. Unlike malachite, it does not occur in sufficiently large compact masses to feature widely for ornamental purposes. It was used in ancient times in Asia to make blue paints for murals and it is still used as a pigment today. An attractive stone called *azurmalachite* is an interbanded form of azurite and malachite. A popular form occurs at Copper Queen Mine, Bisbee, Arizona, USA. Fine crystals of azurite are found at Chessy, near Lyon, France, hence the alternative name chessylite.

Aggregate of azurite with malachite

Azurite

Crystals of azurite with green malachite

Encrusting form

	AZURITE	Occurrence	as a secondary mineral in the oxidized zone of copper deposits along with malachite and its associated minerals; less widely distributed than malachite
*Colour	azure-blue, paler when earthy, darker in crystals		
Lustre	vitreous to adamantine		
Transparency	transparent to translucent		
Streak	light blue		
Hardness	3.5 – 4	Examples	fine crystals at Chessy (France), Tsumeb (Namibia), Bisbee, Arizona (USA), Redruth, Cornwall (England), Laurium (Greece), Romania, Siberia
Cleavage	good		
Fracture	conchoidal		
Habit	crystals either tabular or short prismatic, often complex and malformed; as radiating aggregates; also dull and earthy		
Specific gravity	3.8		
Twinning	rare		
*Other tests	soluble with effervescence in dilute hydrochloric acid		
Crystal system	monoclinic		
Alteration	to malachite		

$BaCO_3$ **Witherite**

When available in sufficient quantities, witherite is an ore of barium. It is used in speciality glasses and for producing finely divided barium sulphate. It was named after a seventeenth-century mineralogist W. Withering, who discovered it. Witherite is always twinned, forming pseudohexagonal pyramids. These often show deep horizontal striations, giving the appearance of a stack of pyramids. It is distinguished from its close relative *strontianite* by a flame test, which shows green for witherite but crimson for strontianite. Like other barium-containing minerals, it is fairly dense (see baryte). It is found mainly as a gangue mineral in lead-zinc ore fields.

Radiating form

Massive form

Twinned crystals

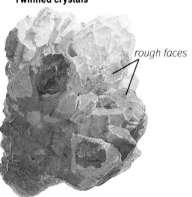

rough faces

	WITHERITE		
Colour	colourless to grey, or pale yellow to brown		in dilute hydrochloric acid; gives green flame test; may fluoresce or phosphoresce in ultraviolet light
Lustre	vitreous, resinous on fracture surfaces		
Transparency	transparent to translucent	**Crystal system**	orthorhombic
Streak	white	**Occurrence**	uncommon; in low-temperature hydrothermal veins with barytes, galena and anglesite
Hardness	3 – 3.5		
Cleavage	distinct		
Fracture	uneven	**Examples**	good crystals at Alston Moor, Cumberland and Hexham, Northumberland, (England) and Rosiclaire, Illinois (USA); masses at El Portal, California (USA) and Siberia (USSR)
Habit	crystals always twinned with pseudo-hexagonal form, deep horizontal striations sometimes making them look like a stack of pyramids; massive, granular, columnar, botryoidal		
Twinning	ubiquitous		
*Specific gravity	4.3		
*Other tests	dissolves with effervescence		

Smithsonite $ZnCO_3$

When it has good colouring (especially translucent green) or banding, smithsonite, an ore of zinc, is used as an ornamental stone. The yellow variety contains cadmium and is known as *turkey-fat ore*. Smithsonite is produced by the action of water rich in zinc salts on carbonate rocks. The salt is usually zinc sulphate, which is produced by the oxidation of sphalerite (zinc sulphide). Smithsonite used to be called calamine, though this name is now generally used for a pink powder used in lotions and ointments. This powder is a mixture of smithsonite and zinc silicates. Smithsonite is named after James Smithson (1765–1829), the British mineralogist who founded the Smithsonian Institution in Washington DC.

Yellow encrustation

Green encrustation

White encrustation

Smithsonite

	SMITHSONITE	
Colour	greyish white to shades of grey or brown; also apple green to bluish green	oxidized zone of hydrothermal veins derived from primary sulphides, particularly sphalerite; often associated with malachite, azurite, cerussite, anglesite, pyromorphite and mimetite
Lustre	vitreous	
Transparency	translucent	
Streak	white	
Hardness	4–4.5	
***Cleavage**	rhombohedral, perfect	
Fracture	uneven	**Examples** Alston Moor, Cumberland, and Mendip Hills, Somerset, (England), Leadhills, Lanarkshire (Scotland), Leadville, Colorado (USA), Southern Kazakhstan (USSR), Tsumeb (Namibia), Santander (Spain), Attiki (Greece), Sardinia
Habit	rhombohedral crystals with rough, curved faces, uncommon; massive in botryoidal, reniform or stalactitic encrustations	
***Specific gravity**	4.4–4.5	
***Other tests**	dissolves with effervescence in dilute hydrochloric acid	
Crystal system	trigonal	
Occurrence	secondary mineral in the	

Baryte is also known as barytes, barite, and heavy spar, because of its high density. In fact, the term baryte comes from the Greek word *baros* which means 'heavy'. Baryte is used in the manufacture of paint and paper, and is the greatest single source of the metallic element barium. Large amounts of baryte are used in the oil industry to make drilling muds. Baryte is often found in a fairly pure state with other gangue minerals (mining waste), such as calcite, fluorite and quartz, in deposits of metal ores, especially those of lead and zinc. Roseate clusters of baryte crystals, found as concretions in some sandstones in Oklahoma and Kansas, are called 'desert roses', the same name given for similar features formed from gypsum.

Cockscomb form

Thin, tabular crystals

Tabular crystals

	BARYTE		
Colour	colourless to white, often tinged with other colours, commonly yellow, red and brown, sometimes bluish	**Twinning**	uncommon
		*Specific gravity	4.3 – 4.6
		*Other tests	gives yellow-green flame test; insoluble in water or hydrochloric acid
Lustre	vitreous, pearly on cleavage	**Crystal system**	orthorhombic
Transparency	transparent to translucent	**Occurrence**	in veins and as a gangue mineral in ore deposits of lead, copper, zinc, silver, iron and nickel; as veins and nodules in limestones and marls; forms a cement in some sandstones
Streak	colourless		
Hardness	3 – 3.5		
*Cleavage	perfect parallel to base plane, good parallel to prism faces		
Fracture	uneven; brittle		
*Habit	tabular, sometimes prismatic when crystalline; often massive; sometimes fibrous or lamellar in clusters, or granular and stalagmitic; can have an attractive cockscomb-like appearance	**Examples**	crystals up to 1 m (3.3 ft) found in the North Pennines and Cornwall (England), Pribran (Czechoslovakia), Transylvania (Romania), Freiberg (Germany)

Gypsum $CaSO_4.2H_2O$

Gypsum is the most common sulphate mineral. It is usually the first evaporite mineral to be precipitated from water due to its poor solubility. Varieties include *selenite*, which is colourless and transparent, *satin spar*, the fibrous form, and *alabaster*, used for ornaments, which is massive and granular. Gypsum 'desert roses' are formed of interpenetrating platy crystals enclosing sand grains. These popular collectors' items are found in Morocco, Tunisia and the USA, in Arizona and New Mexico. Gypsum is used in plasters, including plaster of Paris, in fertilizers, and as a filler in such materials as crayons, paints and paper.

Aggregate of crystals

Desert rose

Crystals of selenite

	GYPSUM		
Colour	colourless or white, shades of grey, yellow or pink		hydrochloric acid
		Crystal system	monoclinic
Lustre	vitreous, pearly on cleavage faces	**Alteration**	to and from anhydrite
		Occurrence	in bedded deposits with other evaporites; important cap-rock on salt domes; small amounts in volcanic areas where sulphuric acid (from pyrite decay) reacts with limestones
Transparency	transparent to translucent		
Streak	white		
*Hardness	2 (easily scratched with a fingernail)		
*Cleavage	one perfect, two good, giving rhomb-shaped fragments		
Habit	simple tabular crystals, often with curved faces; rosette-like aggregates and fibrous or granular masses	**Examples**	widespread but including Stassfurt (Germany), Paris basin (France), Nova Scotia (Canada), New York, Michigan, Utah, Iowa, Texas and California (USA), West Urals, North Caucasus, Uzbekistan (USSR), Chihuahua (Mexico), Bologna, Pavia and Sicily (Italy)
Twinning	'swallow-tail' contact twins common		
Specific gravity	2.3		
Other tests	flakes are somewhat flexible; dissolves in warm, dilute		

Anhydrite is the form of calcium sulphate containing no water in its crystal structure. (Gypsum is the hydrated form.) In fact, its name is derived from the Greek *anhydras*, meaning 'without water'. Anhydrite is an evaporite mineral deposited from seawater at temperatures above 42°C (108°F). It is also formed when gypsum is dehydrated by a rise in temperature following burial. The reverse process, by which anhydrite is altered to become gypsum, occurs when anhydrite is exposed to water and cooler temperatures. Not surprisingly, anhydrite has much the same uses as gypsum. It is used as a source of sulphuric acid and as a filler in paper, and in various plasters. Treated with ammonia, it produces ammonium sulphate fertilizer. As with gypsum, the name anhydrite can be used for the rock in evaporite deposits as well as the mineral. Rock anhydrite is used as polished slabs for interior facing. Anhydrite and gypsum will turn a flame brick-red due to the calcium present.

Banded form

Massive form

ANHYDRITE		
Colour	colourless to bluish when transparent; white, pink or mauve when massive; often discoloured by impurities	
Lustre	vitreous to pearly	
Transparency	transparent to translucent	
Streak	white	
*Hardness	3–3.5	
*Cleavage	three good cleavages at right angles	
Fracture	uneven; splintery	
Habit	usually massive and granular, but can be fibrous or lamellar; crystals rare	
Twinning	common	
*Specific gravity	2.9–3 (higher than calcite)	
Crystal system	orthorhombic	
Alteration	hydrates to gypsum	
Occurrence	forms stratified bodies in the lower parts of evaporite deposits; abundant in cap-rock of salt domes; smaller amounts in hydrothermal veins and vesicles in igneous rocks	
Examples	as caps to salt domes in Louisiana and Texas (USA); in stratified salt deposits in Stassfurt (Germany), Paris basin (France), Poland, Austria and India; purple crystals at Bex (Switzerland)	

Celestine $SrSO_4$

Celestine, the chief ore of strontium, got its name from the Latin word for 'celestial', after the beautiful pale blue colour shown by some of its finest crystals. Strontium and its salts are used in fireworks and flares to impart a strong crimson colour. The crimson colouration of the flame is one of the tests used for identifying strontium salts. White crystals weighing 2–3 kg (4–7 lb) and measuring 50–75 cm (20–30 in) are found at Put-in-Bay, Ohio, USA. Strontium and the mineral strontianite ($SrCO_3$) are named after Strontian in Argyllshire, Scotland. Celestine is also known as celestite.

Tabular crystals

pyramid faces **Prismatic crystals**

Celestine with sulphur

	CELESTINE	
Colour	colourless to pale blue	
Lustre	vitreous, pearly on cleavage	
Transparency	transparent to translucent	
Streak	white	
Hardness	3–3.5	
*Cleavage	basal, perfect; prismatic, good	
Fracture	imperfectly conchoidal; very brittle	
Habit	tabular or prismatic crystals; may be fibrous or granular	
*Specific gravity	3.9–4	
*Other tests	insoluble in acids; gives crimson flame test; may fluoresce under ultraviolet light	
Crystal system	orthorhombic	
Occurrence	in marls and other sediments associated with sulphur and	with such evaporite minerals as gypsum, anhydrite and halite; gangue mineral in hydrothermal veins with galena and sphalerite; sometimes as concretions in clay and marl, in cavities in basic lavas and in the cap-rock of salt domes
Examples		bluish crystals at Yate, near Bristol (England) and in the gypsum and sulphur deposits of Agrivagento (Sicily) and Perticara (Italy); large crystals found at Put-in-Bay and Strontian Island, Lake Erie (USA); in basalt cavities at Vicenza (Italy) and in pegmatites in Bohemia and Madagascar

This important lead ore was first found at Porys Mine on the island of Anglesey, Wales, after which it is named. Like most lead minerals, it has a high specific gravity. It is a secondary mineral, formed most often by the oxidation of a primary deposit of galena. It may occur as granular aggregates surrounding a core of galena, with concentric layers of anglesite identifiable by slight colour changes. Anglesite is often associated with other minerals, especially cerussite, copper carbonates, copper oxides, mimetite and pyromorphite. It can be distinguished from the carbonate mineral cerussite ($PbCO_3$) by the lack of reaction as it dissolves in nitric acid. Fine crystals come from Tsumeb, Namibia, Musen, Germany, and the Wheatley mine, Phoenixville, Pennsylvania, USA. The rare black, white and yellow prismatic crystals from Monteponi, Sardinia are famous among collectors. Because of its toxicity and discoloration, lead sulphate has been replaced by titanium oxide as a white pigment in paint.

Adamantine crystals

Greyish-white, opaque crystals

	ANGLESITE	Crystal system	orthorhombic
Colour	colourless to white; may be tinged yellow, grey or blue	**Occurrence**	common in the oxidized zone of lead deposits in association with galena; as granular aggregates surrounding a core of galena; very rarely as a sublimate from volcanic activity
***Lustre**	adamantine, sometimes resinous		
Transparency	transparent to translucent		
Streak	white		
Hardness	2.5 – 3		
Cleavage	basal, perfect; prismatic, distinct		
Fracture	conchoidal; brittle	**Examples**	most famous are Broken Hill, NSW, (Australia) and Tsumeb (Namibia); others include Matlock, Derbyshire, (England), Leadhills, Lanarkshire (Scotland), Musen, Westphalia (Germany), Phoenixville, Pennsylvania and Tintic, Utah (USA), Los Lamentos, Chihuahua (Mexico)
Habit	crystals often found prismatic, tabular or pyramidal; massive, compact and granular		
***Specific gravity**	6.2 – 6.4		
Other tests	often yellow fluorescence under ultraviolet light; dissolves slowly in dilute nitric acid		

Scheelite $CaWO_4$

Scheelite is an important ore of tungsten, especially in the USA. Tungsten is used to harden steels for use in high-speed tools and engine components, and to prepare tungsten carbides, abrasives which are second only to diamonds in hardness. Metallic tungsten has a high melting point – 3410°C (6170°F) – and is used in lamp filaments and spark plugs. Scheelite is named after K.W. Scheele, the eighteenth century Swedish chemist who discovered tungsten. Occurring alongside scheelite in high temperature veins and pegmatites is the related mineral wolframite $(Fe,MnWO_4)$. Wolframite is a grey-black to brownish black, monoclinic mineral of high specific gravity (7–7.5) which shows one good cleavage. Outside the USA it is the principal ore of tungsten. The name wolframite comes from the German word *wolfram*, meaning 'tungsten'. Scheelite can be confused with quartz, with which it is commonly associated, but is distinguished by the characteristic electric blue to yellow fluorescence under ultraviolet light.

Wolframite

Scheelite in calcite

	SCHEELITE
*Colour	yellowish white to brownish
Lustre	adamantine or vitreous
Transparency	transparent to opaque
Streak	white
Hardness	4.5–5
Cleavage	good, parallel to pyramid
Fracture	conchoidal to uneven; brittle
*Habit	small pyramidal crystals, also massive, granular or columnar
Twinning	penetration twins, common
*Specific gravity	5.9–6.1
Other tests	fluorescence bluish white in ultraviolet light; thermoluminescent
Crystal system	tetragonal
Occurrence	a high-temperature mineral found in quartz veins and greisens close to granites; associated with wolframite, cassiterite, molybdenite, mica, fluorite, topaz etc; in contact metamorphosed limestones with garnet, vesuvianite, sphene, hornblende and epidote
Examples	Carrock Mine, Cumbria, and Cornwall (England); in contact metamorphosed limestones in Humboldt Range, Nevada (USA); in low-temperature veins in Bridge River, British Columbia (Canada); New South Wales (Australia), Monroe, Connecticut, Arizona, California and White Pine, Nevada (USA)

$Ca_5(PO_4)_3(F,Cl,OH)$ Apatite

Apatite is a widely distributed mineral occurring as fluorapatite (F), chloroapatite (Cl) and hydroxylapatite (OH). Its name comes from the Greek *apatao*, meaning 'deceit', because it may be mistaken for other minerals. It is distinguished from beryl and quartz by its lustre and lower hardness. Clear, well-coloured apatites are sometimes used as gemstones, such as 'asparagus stones', but they are rather soft. Apatite is the main constituent of bones and teeth, and in fluorine-bearing forms, is resistant to decay, which is why drinking water is fluoridized. Apatite is used in the manufacture of fertilizers and in the chemical industry.

Hexagonal crystal

Colourless crystals

Apatite crystals in calcite

	APATITE		
Colour	pale sea-green or bluish green, also yellow, brown, violet	***Crystal system**	hexagonal
*Lustre	vitreous to sub-resinous	**Occurrence**	a common accessory mineral in rocks; occurs as large crystals in pegmatites; extensive deposits of phosphate rock may be interbedded with other sedimentary rocks
Transparency	transparent to opaque		
Streak	white		
*Hardness	5		
Cleavage	basal, very poor		
Fracture	conchoidal or uneven; brittle		
Habit	usually in prismatic or needle-like crystals, sometimes tabular; also massive, mammillated or concretionary	**Examples**	good crystals at Wilberforce, Ontario (Canada), Knappenwand (Austria), Cerro de Mercado, Durango (Mexico); Quebec (Canada), the Kola Peninsula (USSR), Bukusu (Uganda); at Kiruna (Sweden); sedimentary phosphates important in Florida (USA), Egypt, Morocco and Tunisia
Specific gravity	3.2		
Other tests	fluorescent under ultraviolet light, in brown, orange, or yellow; may phosphoresce and thermoluminesce; soluble in hydrochloric acid		

Turquoise $CuAl_6(PO_4)_4(OH)_8.5H_2O$

Turquoise is a semi-precious blue gemstone. It is often mottled, with brown or black veinlets. It can be distinguished from the mineral crysocolla by its greater hardness. Care must be taken when handling it, because specimens can alter to an unattractive green if heated too much – due to friction when polishing – or on exposure to sunlight. It is also sensitive to soap, water and grease. Turquoise was used in Ancient Egyptian jewellery. American Indians also used it, typically in silver jewellery. Its name comes from the French *pierre turquoise*, meaning 'Turkish stone'. It was so called because it was brought into Europe via Turkey.

Turquoise in limonite

Turquoise

Turquoise

	TURQUOISE	Examples	Kuh-i-Nishapur, Neyshabur (Iran), Queensland, Victoria and New South Wales (Australia), River Umba Valley (Tanzania), Los Cerillos, New Mexico, and Nevada (USA)
*Colour	sky-blue or blue-green		
Lustre	crystals, vitreous; waxy when massive		
Transparency	almost opaque		
Streak	white or pale greenish		
Hardness	5–6		
Cleavage	good		
Fracture	conchoidal		
Habit	crystals rare and very small; usually massive in veins, concretions or encrustations		
Specific gravity	2.6–2.8		
Crystal system	triclinic		
Occurrence	secondary mineral in veins and pockets in alumunium-rich rocks, often igneous which have undergone considerable alterations, usually in arid regions		

Zn_2SiO_4 Willemite

Willemite is a valuable ore of zinc. It is mined at Franklin Furnace, New Jersey, USA where it occurs in a crystalline limestone. At this locality it is associated with two other zinc minerals – zincite and franklinite – which are virtually restricted to this deposit. Zincite (ZnO) is deep red to orange-yellow in colour, with an orange-yellow streak. Franklinite ($(Zn,Fe,Mn)(Fe,Mn)_2O_4$) is iron black and is usually identified by its association with willemite and zincite. Willemite shows a characteristic strong green fluorescence under ultraviolet light. A manganese-bearing variety is called *troostite*. Willemite was named after King Willem Frederik I of the Netherlands.

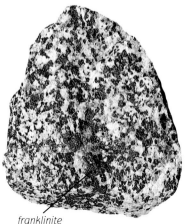

franklinite

Willemite and franklinite

Troostite in marble

Green willemite in calcite

calcite

	WILLEMITE	
*Colour	greenish yellow usual, can be brown or nearly white when pure	
Lustre	vitreous to resinous	
Transparency	transparent to almost opaque	
Hardness	5.5	
Cleavage	two imperfect cleavages	
Fracture	uneven	
Habit	prismatic crystals. Usually massive, granular	
Specific gravity	4–4.1	
*Other tests	usually strongly fluorescent under ultraviolet light	
Crystal system	trigonal	
Occurrence	found in crystalline limestone, possibly forming from the metamorphism of smithsonite or hemimorphite,	

($Zn_4(Si_2O_7)(OH)_2.H_2O$); in small amounts in the oxidized zone of zinc deposits; associated with zincite and franklinite

Examples major deposit at Franklin and Sterling Hill, New Jersey (USA); others at Moresnet and Vieille Montagne (Belgium), Greenland, South Africa, Zaire and Zambia

Olivine (Mg,Fe)₂SiO₄

Olivine is the name for a group of minerals. They vary from the magnesian olivine *forsterite* to the iron olivine *fayalite*. But the most common olivine is of intermediate composition and has a pleasant olive-green colour, from which its name is derived. Olivine is an important rock-forming mineral. It is an essential mineral in basic igneous rocks, such as olivine gabbro, and ultrabasic (silica-poor) rocks such as alkali olivine basalt and peridotite. Gem-quality specimens, called *peridot*, were used in the Middle Ages to decorate church robes and plates. They are now used in jewellery.

Olivine nodule

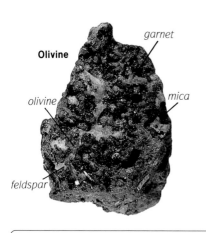

Olivine

olivine

garnet

mica

feldspar

Peridot

	OLIVINE	
*Colour	shades of green, especially olive; forsterite, white or yellow; fayalite, brown or black	oxidized crystals may look reddish
Lustre	vitreous	
Transparency	transparent to translucent	
Streak	colourless or white	
Hardness	6.5 (fayalite) – 7 (forsterite)	
Cleavage	usually poorly developed	
*Fracture	conchoidal; brittle	
Habit	good crystals rare; usually isolated grains in igneous rocks, or granular masses	
Twinning	uncommon	
Specific gravity	3.2 (forsterite) – 4.4 (fayalite)	
Other tests	decomposed by hydrochloric acid, forming a gel	
Crystal system	orthorhombic	
Alteration	readily to serpentine;	

Occurence an important rock-forming mineral in basic and ultrabasic igneous rocks; fayalite occurs rarely in some quartz-bearing igneous rocks; forsterite in metamorphosed siliceous dolomite; olivine in some meteorites

Examples peridot in Eifel (Germany), on St. John's Island in the Red Sea (Egypt), in Mogok (Myanmar, formerly Burma); fayalite in rhyolites in Yellowstone National Park, Wyoming (USA) and in granite pegmatites in the Mourne Mountains (Ireland); forsterite on Skye (Scotland)

(Mg,Fe, Mn)$_3$Al$_2$Si$_3$O$_{12}$ Garnet: Pyralspite Garnets

Garnet is the name for a family of minerals. Chemically, they are divided into two groups: pyralspite garnets and grandite garnets. Pyralspite garnets are *pyrope* (magnesium and aluminium), *almandine* (iron and aluminium) and *spessartine* (manganese and aluminium). Garnets are used as gemstones in jewellery and are often given incorrect names, such as 'Cape ruby' or 'Arizona spinel'. The beautiful deep red pyrope is one of the most popular. Almandine, one of the most widespread varieties, often occurs as large, perfect crystals. Spessartine, one of the more precious gemstones, is popular for its yellowish-orange colour.

**Almandine
in schist**

**Three faces of
rhombdodecahedron**

**Spessartine
in marble**

	GARNET
Colour	variable; red to nearly black (pyrope), red-brown to black (almandine), dark-red to brownish red (spessartine)
Lustre	vitreous to resinous
Transparency	transparent to translucent
Streak	whitish
Hardness	6.5–7.5
Cleavage	absent
Fracture	subconchoidal or uneven
Habit	crystals common; dodeca-hedra or icositetrahedra
Specific gravity	3.7–4.3
Crystal system	cubic
Occurrence	pyrope in ultrabasic igneous rocks and in detrital deposits; almandine common in medium- and high-grade schists and gneisses derived from argillaceous rocks, in metamorphosed igneous rocks, and in heavy detrital residues in sediments; spessartine rarely in acid igneous rocks and in skarn deposits
Examples	pyrope in Kimberley (South Africa), Yakut (Siberia), Arizona and New Mexico (USA); gem almandine in Sri Lanka and India; spessartine in Sri Lanka, Madagascar, Upper Myanmar (formerly Burma), Brazil and Tanzania; also the Spessart Mountains and the Harz Mountains (Germany), and St. Marcel, Piedmont (Italy)

Garnet: Ugrandite Garnets $Ca_3(Al,Cr,Fe)_2Si_3O_{12}$

The ugrandite garnets are *uvarovite* (calcium and chromium), *grossular* (calcium and aluminium) and *andradite* (calcium and iron). Most crystals are mixed, so that there is a partial replacement of some elements by others. The beautiful, deep emerald-green uvarovite is one of the rarest gemstones. Grossular gets its name from the botanical name for 'gooseberry', which it resembles in colour and shape. It is unusual among garnets in that it luminesces strongly in ultraviolet light. The green variety of andradite used as a gemstone is called *demantoid*, after the Old French word *diamant*, meaning diamond. Demantoid has a high dispersion comparable with diamond. Garnet is derived from the Latin *granatus* meaning 'like a grain'.

Grossular

Grossular

Uvarovite

Andradite

	GARNET
Colour	bright green (uvarovite); colourless to white, pale green, yellow brown or pink (grossular); yellow, green, brown or black (andradite)
Lustre	vitreous to resinous
Transparency	translucent
Streak	whitish
Hardness	6.5 – 7.5
Cleavage	absent
Fracture	subconchoidal or uneven
Habit	crystals common; dodeca-hedra or icositetrahedra
Specific gravity	3.4 – 4.1 depending on composition
Crystal system	cubic
Occurrence	uvarovite is found in serpentinites rich in chromite; grossular occurs in marbles associated with calcite, diopside, wollastonite and vesuvianite; andradite is produced by contact metamorphism of limestones accompanied by the introduction of iron; also in syenite, serpentinite and chlorite schists
Examples	uvarovite in Sysert, the Urals (USSR), Outokumpu (Finland), Texas and California (USA), Quebec (Canada); grossular crystals in gem-bearing sands of Sri Lanka, Telemarken (Norway) Chihuahua (Mexico); andradite in the Urals (USSR), Val Malenco (Italy), Tanzania and Zaire

$ZrSiO_4$ **Zircon**

Zircon is an ore of the metal zirconium, which is used in the construction of nuclear reactors. It has long been mined as a gemstone, though it did not become fashionable until the 1920s. The reddish-brown variety is called *hyacinth* or *jacinth*. Its main shortcoming is its brittle nature, and so the edges of cut stones are easily damaged. Zircon has variable properties. Scientists now know that these result from the presence of radioactive elements – thorium and uranium – substituting for zirconium. This radiation alters the arrangement of atoms in the crystal, giving a weakened 'metamict' form. The name zircon is thought to be derived from the Persian *zar* meaning 'gold', and *gun*, meaning 'colour'.

Tetragonal crystals

pyramid face

prism face

Knee-shaped twinned crystal

Hyacinth

	ZIRCON	Occurrence	one of the commonest
*Colour	usually light brown to red-brown; also yellowish, green, colourless or purplish		accessories of acid and intermediate igneous rocks; also in schists and gneisses; commonly occurs as rounded detrital grains in sands and sandstones
Lustre	vitreous to adamantine		
Transparency	transparent to translucent, occasionally nearly opaque		
Streak	colourless	Examples	in alkaline rocks of the Kola Peninsula (USSR); in syenites and pegmatites of Arendal and Langesund (Norway); in gem gravels in Thailand; in beach sands in New South Wales (Australia); good crystals in Matura (Sri Lanka) and in gold gravels in the Urals (USSR); large crystals at Renfrew (Canada) and Litchfield, Maine (USA)
*Hardness	7.5 (6.5 metamict form)		
Cleavage	prismatic, indistinct		
Fracture	conchoidal; very brittle		
*Habit	prismatic crystals terminated by pyramids		
Twinning	common, forming knee-shaped twins		
*Specific gravity	4.6 – 4.7		
Other tests	coloured varieties become colourless and transparent when heated		
Crystal system	tetragonal		

Sillimanite Al_2SiO_5

Mineralogists describe sillimanite, kyanite and andalusite as *polymorphs* – that is, these minerals have the same chemical formula but different structures and properties. For example, they are stable under different temperatures, sillimanite being the high-temperature form. All three break down on heating to 1300°C (2372°F) to form a mineral called *mullite* and a siliceous glass. All three minerals are mined for conversion to mullite which is used in making refractory (heat-resistant) bricks and porcelain. Large prismatic crystals of sillimanite may stand out on weathered rock surfaces. Intergrowths of the fibrous form *fibrolite* with quartz are easily seen on weathered surfaces as they are pure white. Large masses of almost pure sillimanite (85 per cent) have been mined in India. Gem-quality sillimanite is rare, but it is occasionally used in jewellery and the manufacture of carved figurines. The name is in honour of Benjamin Silliman, professor of chemistry in the nineteenth century.

Fibrolite

Prismatic crystals

	SILLIMANITE
Colour	greyish white, yellow, brown, greyish green
Lustre	vitreous to almost adamantine
Transparency	transparent to translucent
Streak	colourless
Hardness	6–7
Cleavage	good, parallel to side face
Fracture	uneven
*Habit	long slender prisms or in a felted mass of fibres called fibrolite
Specific gravity	3.2–3.3
Crystal system	orthorhombic
Occurrence	in regional metamorphic rocks formed from clays (i.e. rich in aluminium), also occasionally in the inner zone of hornfelses

Examples blue, transparent sillimanite found at Mogok (Myanmar, formerly Burma); greyish green varieties in gravels in Sri Lanka; water-worn masses in diamond-bearing sands at Minas Gerais (Brazil); massive fibrous sillimanite cobbles from Clearwater River valley, Idaho (USA); Maldan (Bohemia), Freiburg (Saxony)

Al_2SiO_5 Andalusite

Andalusite is the low-pressure, low-density form of the three aluminium silicate polymorphs (see sillimanite and kyanite). Petrologists find it a useful indicator of the conditions of metamorphism that existed when the rocks containing it were formed. Andalusite has been mined in large quantities in California and is used as a raw material for refractory (heat-resistant) linings. It is also used in high-temperature electrical insulators and in special acid-resistant porcelains. Transparent crystals may be used as gems. Well known examples are the rich green pebbles of andalusite found in Sri Lanka and Minas Gerais, Brazil. These crystals may show colour changes to reddish oranges owing to the property *pleochroism*, which is pronounced in andalusite. The large crystals found in Andalusia, Spain – from which the mineral is named – are mainly altered to white mica and quartz. Crystals up to 20 cm (8 in) long and 5 cm (2 in) thick occur at Lisenz, Austria. When broken across, the variety *chiastolite* shows a black cross, which is formed from carbonaceous impurities. Chiastolite is common in schists near Santiago de Compostela in Spain. It was once worn as an amulet.

Prismatic crystals of andalusite

inclusions form cross-shape

Chiastolite

	ANDALUSITE		
Colour	white, pink, pearl-grey, may be green or brown		low pressure regional metamorphism; in pegmatites where it may be associated with corundum, tourmaline and topaz
Lustre	vitreous		
Transparency	translucent to opaque		
Streak	white	**Examples**	crystals up to 20 cm (8 in) long at Lisenz (Austria); in radial aggregates in pegmatites at Velke Mezirici, Moravia (Czechoslovakia); also in Murzinka, the Urals (USSR), Minas Gerais (Brazil), Bimbourne (Australia); chiastolite in Cumbria (England) and near Nerchinsk, Transbaikalia (USSR); large crosses with diagonals up to 8 cm (3 in) from Keiva, Kola Peninsula (USSR)
*Hardness	7.5		
Cleavage	prismatic, distinct		
Fracture	uneven; tough, brittle		
*Habit	prismatic crystals of square cross-section, also granular or massive		
Specific gravity	3.2		
Crystal system	orthorhombic		
Alteration	to a shimmer aggregate of white mica and quartz, which often coats the crystals		
Occurrence	in clays which have been affected either by thermal metamorphism or by		

Kyanite Al_2SiO_5

Kyanite is also known as disthene, meaning 'double strength'. This refers to the fact that the hardness along the length of kyanite crystals is less than the hardness across them. This is the mineral's most characteristic feature. Kyanite is mined in several parts of the world for use as a refractory material. Transparent crystals are occasionally used in jewellery. The most valued colours are deep cornflower-blue, pale azure-blue and bluish-green. Like the other aluminium silicate polymorphs, kyanite is an indicator of metamorphic conditions. It is formed at moderate temperatures and at moderate to high pressures in pelitic rocks, and is often associated with garnet, staurolite and corundum. The name is derived from the Greek word *kyanos*, meaning 'a dark blue substance'.

Bladed crystals

Kyanite

Kyanite

kyanite porphyroblasts

	KYANITE	
*Colour	blue, sometimes white or colourless at margins	
Lustre	vitreous, pearly on cleavage surfaces	
Transparency	transparent to subtranslucent	
Streak	white	
*Hardness	5–7 varying with direction	
*Cleavage	two good cleavages	
Fracture	brittle	
*Habit	as flat, bladed crystals in schists and gneisses, and as radiating rosettes in quartz	
Specific gravity	3.5–3.7	
Twinning	frequent	
Crystal system	triclinic	
Alteration	to a shimmer aggregate of white mica and quartz	
Occurrence	in regionally metamorphosed rocks, i.e. schists, gneisses, eclogites and amphibolites; may be associated with garnet or staurolite; also in associated pegmatites and quartz veins; a detrital mineral	
Examples	good blue crystals at Pizzo Forno, Candon Ticino, (Switzerland); enormous crystals at Minas Gerais (Brazil); green crystals up to 30 cm (12 in) long at Machakos (Kenya); large deposits at Chesterfield, Massachusetts, Litchfield Connecticut and Yancey County, North Carolina (USA), also India, Kenya and Australia	

eople have valued topaz as a gemstone
nce the times of ancient Greece. Its
ualities are its hardness, pleasant
olour and high lustre. It occurs in a
ariety of delicate colours, the most
rized being pink, blue and honey-
ellow. Some stones change colour on
eating. For example, yellow topaz from
razil turns red if heated to 300°–450°C
72°–842°F) and cooled slowly to
revent cracking. Topaz crystals weigh
p to 300 kg (661 lb). The largest cut
paz, a pale blue Brazilian Princess,
as found at Teófilo Otoni, north of Rio
e Janeiro. It weighed 4265.5 g (21,327
arats or 150 oz).

**Massive
white topaz**

**opaz and quartz
n orthoclase**

quartz   orthoclase

**Yellow topaz
crystal**

*striated
prism
faces*

TOPAZ

Colour	colourless, straw-yellow, pale blue or green
Lustre	vitreous
Transparency	transparent to sub-translucent
Streak	colourless
*Hardness	8
*Cleavage	basal, perfect
Fracture	sub-conchoidal to uneven
*Habit	prismatic crystals, vertically striated; also columnar or granular
*Specific gravity	3.4–3.6
Other tests	sometimes fluorescent in yellow, cream or pale green
Crystal system	orthorhombic
Occurrence	a pneumatolytic mineral, in granite and pegmatites, associated with tourmaline, cassiterite and fluorspar; also as round translucent pebbles in alluvium as a secondary deposit
Examples	the largest crystals come from Minas Gerais (Brazil) and Albaschka (Siberia); azure-blue topazes from Murzinka near Sverdlovsk in the Urals (USSR); placer deposits from the River Sanarka (Urals), Sri Lanka and Durango (Mexico); good crystals from Mino Province (Japan); major localities in the USA are Pikes Peak (Colorado), Thomas Range (Utah) and San Diego County (California)

Staurolite $(Fe,Mg)_2(Al,Fe)_9(Si_4O_{20})(O,OH)_2$

The term staurolite comes from the Greek word *stauros* meaning 'cross', because the mineral is famous for its cross-, plus- or X-shaped interpenetrant twinned crystals. Cross- or plus-shaped twins are known as 'fairy stones' in North Carolina, USA, and are sold as amulets, although many of these are dyed imitations made from rock. Plus-shaped twins and dark brown, transparent crystals are sometimes used as gemstones. Staurolite occurs as large crystals (*porphyroblasts*) in schists and gneisses formed from argillaceous sediments in which sufficient iron is present. It is commonly associated with kyanite, garnet, tourmaline and sillimanite. It stands out as yellowish brown prisms on weathered rocks.

Interpenetrant twin

Staurolite schist

staurolite porphyroblasts

Staurolite schist

staurolite porphyroblasts

	STAUROLITE		
*Colour	usually reddish brown, also brownish black yellowish brown or grey when altered	Alteration	surfaces often have an earthy coating due to alteration
Lustre	vitreous to resinous	Occurrence	a metamorphic mineral typical of medium temperature regional metamorphism; may occur with kyanite (often as parallel intergrowths), also garnet, tourmaline and sillimanite; also as a detrital mineral in alluvial sands
Transparency	usually translucent to opaque, rarely transparent		
Streak	colourless when fresh		
Hardness	7–7.5		
Cleavage	fair, in one direction		
Fracture	conchoidal to uneven		
Habit	usually in well-developed prismatic crystals		
*Twinning	famous for interpenetrant twins, to give cross-, plus-, or X-shaped twins; rarely massive	Examples	large crystals in Goldenstein (Moravia), Bavaria and Scotland; cruciform twins in Fannin County, Georgia, and at Pilar, New Mexico (USA), and Morbihan (France); in mica schists in Ticino (Switzerland)
Specific gravity	3.4–3.8		
Other tests	infusible, insoluble in acids		
Crystal system	monoclinic		

The name sphene comes from the Greek word *sphen*, meaning 'wedge', because the crystals are commonly wedge-shaped. The mineral is not widely used in jewellery, because the clear green, yellow or brownish stones used as gems are rare. These crystals are brilliant, but they are comparatively soft. Other varieties of sphene may be opaque. Sphene is a source of titanium oxide, which is used as a pigment in paint. Sphene is widely distributed as an accessory mineral in igneous rocks. It also occurs in metamorphic schists, gneisses and marbles. The most economically important occurrence of sphene is in the Kola Peninsula, USSR. The alternative name titanite refers to the high titanium content. The element titanium was named after the Titans, the mythical sons of the Earth.

Massive form

Massive form

Crystals

	SPHENE	
Colour	yellow, green, brown, reddish brown, red or black	
Lustre	vitreous, inclining to adamantine	
Transparency	transparent to opaque	
Streak	white	
Hardness	5–5.5	
Cleavage	moderate, prismatic	
Fracture	conchoidal; brittle	
Habit	disseminated crystals, usually wedge- or envelope-shaped; occurs also in compact or lamellar masses and in disseminated grains	
Twinning	common, giving sharp re-entrant angles	
Specific gravity	3.4–3.6	
Other tests	fuses with swelling on the edges to a dark-coloured glass; partly decomposed by hydrochloric acid, completely by sulphuric acid	
Crystal system	monoclinic	
Alteration	to rutile, ilmenite and others	
Occurrence	an important accessory of many igneous rocks, e.g. hornblende granite, syenite and diorite; also in schists and lime-rich rocks altered by contact metamorphism	
Examples	widely distributed, classic localities in the Alps, e.g. St Gotthard, Tavetsch and Zillerthal; large crystals at Bridgewater, Bucks County, Pennsylvania (USA); gem-quality at Pino Solo, Baja California Norte (Mexico)	

Idocrase $Ca10(Mg,Fe)_2Al_4Si_9O_{34}(OH,F)_4$

Massive forms of idocrase are often mistaken for diopside, epidote or garnet, while crystals resemble minerals of similar colour, such as diopside, green garnet, olivine and tourmaline. Idocrase is essentially a mineral of contact metamorphism. Its high calcium content reflects its occurrence in limestones. It is also called *vesuvianite* after a green variety found in blocks of dolomitic limestone erupted from Mount Vesuvius, Italy. Gem quality crystals are rare, but are extracted for cutting at Litchfield in Pontiac County and Templeton in Ottowa County, Quebec, Canada. Most idocrase used in jewellery is in smoothly polished, rounded shapes. A green, massive variety of idocrase – *californite* – is used as a jade substitute, called *Vesuvian Jade* in the trade. Other forms are a blue variety, *cyprine*, found at Arendal, Norway, and a pale-green, boron-containing variety, *wiluite*, found in Siberia. Transparent crystals are rare. Larger specimens are used for small receptacles and figurines. The name is from the Greek *eidos* meaning 'likeness' and *krasis* meaning 'mixture', alluding to its similarity to other minerals.

striations parallel to length

Dark green, prismatic crystals

Pale brown, striated crystals

IDOCRASE	
Colour	brown to yellow-brown or green; blue form called cyprine
Lustre	vitreous to resinous
Transparency	transparent to translucent
Streak	white
Hardness	6–7
Cleavage	poor
Fracture	uneven; brittle
***Habit**	prismatic crystals often striated lengthwise; also massive, granular or columnar
Specific gravity	3.3–3.4
Crystal system	tetragonal
Occurrence	in contact metamorphosed impure limestones along with grossular garnet, diopside, wollastonite, epidote and calcite
Examples	Zermatt (Swiss Alps), Mount Vesuvius, Monzoni, Piedmont (Italy), Gopfergrun, Fichtelgebirge (Germany), Ciclova (Romania), Arendal (Norway), Akhmatovsk, the Urals (USSR), Litchfield, Quebec and Templeton, Ontario (Canada), Magnet Cove, Arkansas and Sanford, Maine (USA)

Dioptase is a relatively rare emerald-green mineral, sometimes tinged bluish or blackish. It has no industrial importance, but is popular with collectors. It has been called 'copper emerald' or 'the emerald of the poor'. Dioptase crystals mined at Mount Altyn-Tyube, USSR, were first thought to be emeralds. But their low hardness easily distinguishes them from emeralds – one reason why dioptase is not more valued. The crystals found in Zaire, at Reneville, are quite large and may be cut for jewellery. Dioptase has only had general recognition in Europe since it was introduced in 1780 to St. Petersburg, where it was wrongly identified as a variety of emerald called *achrite*. A related copper silicate mineral is *Chrysocolla* ((Cu,Al) $SiO_3.H_2O$), which is probably amorphous. It forms green to blue-green encrustations and fillings of enamel-like or earthy texture. Fine cleavages in dioptase crystals sometimes give a pearly lustre and interesting internal reflections. This accounts for its name which comes from Greek words for 'through' and 'visible'.

Crystals

Crystals

	DIOPTASE	
*Colour	emerald-green	Copiapo (Chile), Mammoth Mine, Tiger, Arizona (USA) and Otavi Range at Guchabo (Namibia)
Lustre	vitreous	
Transparency	transparent to translucent	
Streak	green	
*Hardness	5	
Cleavage	rhombohedral, perfect	
Fracture	conchoidal to uneven, brittle	
Habit	short, prismatic crystals often terminated by rhombohedra; massive	
Specific gravity	3.3	
Crystal system	trigonal	
Occurrence	uncommon; found in the weathered zones of copper sulphide deposits	
Examples	Mount Altyn-Tyube, Kazakhstan (USSR), Reneville (Zaire), minor deposits at Baita (Romania),	

Epidote $Ca_2(Al,Fe)_3Si_3O_{12}(OH)$

Epidote forms a continuous series of minerals, ending with clinozoisite, which contains no iron. Epidote has a characteristic yellow-green colour. It may be mistaken for tourmaline, which lacks cleavage and has a triangular or hexagonal cross-section. *Withamite* is a pink, manganese-bearing epidote found in vesicles and veins in andesite. *Pumpellyite*, a widely distributed, hydrous epidote-like mineral, is found in low-grade metamorphosed tuffs, and also in the vesicles of ancient lavas. *Pistacite* is a pistachio-green variety. Epidote is a widespread mineral. It is common in medium- or low-grade metamorphic rocks which have formed either from calcareous or basic rocks. It occurs in 'saussurite', the alteration product of plagioclase feldspar, and is formed from the alteration of hornblende.

Prismatic crystals of epidote

striations parallel to length

Massive epidote

Withamite

	EPIDOTE		
*Colour	yellowish green to greenish black (epidote); greenish grey (clinozoisite)	**Crystal system**	a black magnetic glass
		Crystal system	monoclinic
Lustre	vitreous	**Occurrence**	found in medium- to low-grade metamorphic rocks; epidote associated with garnet, diopside, idocrase and calcite in impure limestones in contact aureoles; formed by hydrothermal alteration of plagioclase in gabbros; in vesicles in basic lava flows
Transparency	transparent to nearly opaque		
Streak	white or grey–brown		
Hardness	6–7		
Cleavage	one perfect basal cleavage parallel to length of crystals		
Fracture	uneven; brittle		
*Habit	crystals elongated and often striated parallel to length; also massive, fibrous, or granular	**Examples**	good crystals at Untersulzbachtal (Austria); Arendal (Norway), Bourg d'Oisans, Isère (France); pink crystals at Champernotto in Val d'ala, Turin (Italy); and in metabasites in Troodos Mountains (Cyprus)
Twinning	uncommon		
Specific gravity	3.2–3.5 (increasing with iron-content)		
Other tests	epidote fuses with swelling to		

$Ca_2Al_3Si_3O_{12}(OH)$ **Zoisite**

oisite is a member of the epidote group
f minerals, although it belongs to the
rthorhombic rather than the
onoclinic crystal system. *Thulite*, a
ink, manganese-bearing variety from
orway, has been used in jewellery –
hule is an ancient Greek term for far
orthern countries. Transparent,
uish-violet crystals of another variety,
alled *tanzanite*, have been called the
lue treasure of Africa'. They were first
iscovered near Arusha, Tanzania, in
967, and the largest specimen found to
ate weighed 126 carats (25 g).
anzanite can be created artificially by
eating green zoisite to a temperature
f 380°C (716°F), at which it turns blue-
iolet. Zoisite is similar in appearance
nd occurrence to clinozoisite, but is
ess common.

Thulite

**Chrome zoisite
with ruby**

Cut tanzanite

Uncut tanzanite

	ZOISITE	
*Colour	grey to white, pale green or yellow-brown; thulite, rose-pink	
Lustre	vitreous, pearly on cleavage surfaces	
Transparency	transparent to translucent	
Streak	white	
Hardness	6–6.5	
Cleavage	one perfect cleavage	
Fracture	uneven	
Habit	prismatic crystals, often striated parallel to length; also massive, coarse- to fine-bladed or fibrous aggregates	
Specific gravity	3.2–3.4	
Crystal system	orthorhombic	
Occurrence	forms like epidote and clinozoisite as a constituent of saussurite, resulting from the alteration of calcic plagioclases in gabbros; in metamorphic rocks, especially formed either from igneous rocks rich in calcic feldspars, or impure limestones; in metasomatic rocks may be associated with garnet, idocrase and actinolite	
Examples	Sausalpe (Austria), Wyoming (USA) and Yourma Mountains, the Urals (USSR); tanzanite from Tanga Province (Tanzania); thulite at Trondheim and Arendal (Norway), Tennessee and Carolina (USA) and the Austrian Tyrol	

Beryl $Be_3Al_2Si_6O_{18}$

Beryl is one of the oldest known minerals. The most prized variety *emerald* sometimes fetches higher prices than diamond. Emerald was mined in Upper Egypt in about 2000 BC. Queen Cleopatra is supposed to have owned an emerald on which her portrait was engraved. The short-sighted Roman emperor Nero may have used an emerald as a monocle, but historians now think that it was probably made of the pale blue variety *aquamarine*. Most blue aquamarines used in jewellery were originally greenish-yellow. The colour changes when they are heated to 400°–450°C (752°–842°F) and then cooled. Some beryl crystals are enormous. One discovered in Albany, Maine, was 6 m (20 ft) long.

Aquamarine

Pale green beryl

Beryl in feldspar

Emerald

	BERYL		
*Colour	pale green to bright green (emerald), bluish-green (aquamarine), yellow and white	**Alteration**	alters to mica and kaolin
		Occurrence	commonly found as an accessory mineral in acid igneous rocks, such as granite and pegmatite; also in gneiss, schist and slate, in limestone or in secondary deposits
Lustre	vitreous		
Transparency	transparent to translucent, opaque when full of inclusions		
Streak	white		
*Hardness	7.5–8	**Examples**	aquamarines from Brazil, Nerchinsk Mountains, Transbaikalia and Mursinsk, the Urals (USSR); emeralds from near Bogotá (Colombia), and Sverdlovsk (USSR); beryl is found in the Mourne Mountain granite (Ireland)
Cleavage	indistinct, basal		
Fracture	conchoidal to uneven; brittle		
Habit	simple hexagonal prisms, often striated vertically; also columnar, granular, and compact masses and in rounded grains		
Specific gravity	2.6–2.8		
*Crystal system	hexagonal		

$(Mg,Fe)_2Al_4Si_5O_{18}$ Cordierite

he Vikings probably used bluish-white
pecimens of cordierite as navigational
ids. They could tell the points of the
ompass even when the sky was
vercast, because, depending on which
ay it was viewed, the mineral changed
olour in polarized light. This
istinctive feature is called *pleochroism*.
he variety of cordierite, *dichroite*, may
ppear yellow or deep blue according to
ne way in which it is viewed, while the
iolet-coloured variety is called *iolite*.
lthough gem-quality cordierite is
ttractive and readily available it is not
onsidered valuable and is not widely
sed. The best gemstones come from
Iadagascar and a pale form called
ater sapphire occurs in Sri Lanka. The
on-rich form is called *sekaninaite*.
ranular cordierite resembles quartz,
om which it is distinguished with
ifficulty. Unlike quartz, however, it
an be found enwrapping other crystals.
ordiereite is named after P.L.A.
ordier who described it in detail.

vitreous lustre

Massive form

Cordierite in gneiss

	CORDIERITE	Occurrence	widespread in hornfels
*Colour	light to dark smoky blue and violet; also grey, colourless, green or yellow; pleochroism visible to the naked eye		produced from argillaceous rocks, as oval bluish spots or cavities; also in gneisses and schists where pressure was
Lustre	vitreous to greasy		low; may be found in norite
Transparency	transparent to translucent		or granite, where clay has
Streak	white		been incorporated;
Hardness	7		associated with garnet, mica,
Cleavage	poor in one direction		quartz, andalusite, sillimanite,
Fracture	conchoidal to uneven; brittle		staurolite, chalcopyrite and
Habit	pseudo-hexagonal, short prismatic crystals; often as irregular and rounded grains, looking like quartz	**Examples**	spinel
Twinning	pseudo-hexagonal twins		Banff (Scotland), Falun (Sweden), Bancroft, Ontario (Canada), Collins Hill, Connecticut (USA); blue
Specific gravity	2.6 – 2.8		crystals from Sri Lanka used
Crystal system	orthorhombic		as gemstones (*saphir d'eau*)
Alteration	alters readily to mica, chlorite and talc		

Tourmaline $Na(Mg,Fe,Li,Al,Mn)_3Al_6(BO_3)_3O_{18}(OH,F)_4$

Tourmaline can show a variety of colours, even in a single crystal. The layers of the crystal may be arranged concentrically, parallel to the vertical axis of the crystal, or in longitudinal bands. Such tourmalines are called *moorheads*, or *turkheads* where the last colour is red. Some crystals are strongly pleochroic to the naked eye and are used as gemstones. Others change colour when moved from natural to artificial light. Red tourmaline, introduced to Europe from Sri Lanka in 1703, was found to have the special property of attracting tiny ash particles on heating. These were the first observations of pyroelectricity.

Tourmaline crystals in quartz and apatite

Green crystals

Elongate crystals in quartz

Rubellite

	TOURMALINE
*Colour	usually pitch black or brown, also grey, yellow, green or red, and more rarely colourless or white; colours commonly zoned
Lustre	vitreous to resinous
Transparency	transparent to opaque
Streak	white
Hardness	7–7.5
Cleavage	not well marked
Fracture	conchoidal to uneven; brittle
*Habit	long prismatic crystals of curved triangular cross-section, vertically striated; the two ends of the crystal are often terminated differently; also columnar masses and radiating groups
Specific gravity	2.9–3.2
Other tests	strongly piezoelectric and pyroelectric
Crystal system	trigonal
Alteration	to muscovite, biotite or chlorite
Occurrence	a characteristic mineral of pegmatite dykes in granite, and in schorl formed by pneumatolytic alteration; also common in gneisses, schists and in crystalline limestones and dolomites; a heavy residue in many sedimentary rocks
Examples	excellent crystals in Elba (Italy), Myanmar (formerly Burma), St. Gotthard (Switzerland), Minas Gerais (Brazil), St. Lawrence County, New York (USA)

Pyroxenes are a widespread group of rock-forming silicates. The two main groups are orthopyroxenes and clinopyroxenes. The orthopyroxenes form a chemical series of which the most common are the magnesium-rich *enstatite* (Mg_2SiO_3) and the iron-containing *bronzite* and *hypersthene*. Hypersthene contains up to a 1:1 ratio of magnesium and iron, while bronzite is intermediate between enstatite and hypersthene. Pyroxenes are distinguished from another group of rock-forming silicates called amphiboles by having two cleavages, approximately at right angles to each other. The colour deepens with increasing iron content. Enstatite is usually light green, while hypersthene is a dark, brownish green. Bronzite can be recognised by its characteristic bronze lustre.

Hypersthene

Orthopyroxenes

two cleavages, intersecting at 90°

Bronzite

	ORTHOPYROXENES
*Colour	pale green to dark brownish green or black; bronze lustre for bronzite
Lustre	vitreous
Transparency	translucent to opaque
Hardness	5–6
*Cleavage	prismatic, good cleavages intersect close to right-angles
Fracture	uneven
Habit	stubby prismatic crystals; most often as grains, massive
Specific gravity	3.2–4 (iron-rich pyroxenes are more dense)
Crystal system	orthorhombic
Alteration	to serpentine minerals or fibrous amphibole
Occurrence	mostly as common

constituents of basic and ultrabasic igneous rocks especially easily seen in gabbros and pyroxenites; in some andesites and stony meteorites; in some thermally metamorphosed shales and high-grade regionally metamorphosed rocks

Examples Sierra Nevada, California (USA), Donegal (Northern Ireland), Cima de Gagnone (Switzerland), Troodos (Cyprus) and Cortland Complex, New York (USA); bronzite in Bushveld Complex, Transvaal (South Africa) and Stillwater Complex, Montana (USA)

Clinopyroxenes $Ca(Mg,Fe)Al,Fe,Ti(Si,Al)_2O_6$

Clinopyroxenes are abundant rock-forming minerals. They vary in composition more than orthopyroxenes. *Augite* and *pigeonite* are calcium-poor varieties found in basalts, dolerites and andesites. *Diopside* and *hedenbergite* occur in metamorphic rocks. *Titanaugite*, found in alkali-gabbros and alkali olivine basalts, has a high titanium content and is violet or purple-brown. *Omphacite* is an unusually bright green mineral found in eclogites. Other clinopyroxenes are the sodium-containing *aegerine* ($NaFeSi_2O_6$), *spodumene* ($LiAlSi_2O_6$), an ore of lithium, and *jadeite* ($NaAlSi_2O_6$), which is used as the ornamental stone jade.

Aegerine

Spodumene

Augite crystals *short prismatic crystals*

Hedenbergite

CLINOPYROXENES

Colour	dark green to black (augite)
Lustre	vitreous
Transparency	translucent to opaque
Hardness	5.5 – 6.5
Cleavage	prismatic good, sometimes basal parting present
Fracture	uneven
Habit	stubby crystals of square or eight-sided cross-section; granular, massive
Twinning	common
Specific gravity	3.2 – 3.6
Crystal system	monoclinic
Occurrence	augite is common in such igneous rocks as gabbros, basalts, pyroxenites and diorites; also in some high-grade metamorphic rocks; diopside and hedenbergite occur in a number of metamorphic rocks, diopside in metamorphosed impure limestones, hedenbergite in metamorphosed iron-rich sediments
Examples	augite in Bushveld Complex (South Africa), Skaergaard (Greenland) and Stillwater Complex, Montana (USA); hedenbergite at Cap Calamita, Elba (Italy), Arendal (Norway) and Obira (Japan); diopside at Binnenthal (Switzerland), Vesuvius (Italy), the Zillertal (Austria) and the Urals and Lake Baikal (USSR)

Wollastonite, which was once called *tabular spar*, occurs in impure limestones that have been altered by heat. It often occurs in association with tremolite, from which it can be distinguished by its solubility in hydrochloric acid. Wollastonite is used in refractories and some paints. A related mineral, *rhodonite*, whose formula is $((Mn,Fe,Ca)SiO_3)$, is associated with manganese ore deposits in hydrothermal veins or found in metamorphosed manganese-bearing sediments. Rhodonite is a pink to brown mineral that weathers to black, and is used as a decorative stone. Wollastonite and rhodonite belong to the pyroxenoid group, which are related to the pyroxenes. Wollastonite is named after W.H. Wollaston, the British mineralogist.

Wollastonite

Polished rhodonite

Granular rhodonite

surface alteration to black manganese oxide

	WOLLASTONITE	
*Colour	white or greyish	
Lustre	vitreous	
Transparency	subtransparent to translucent	
Hardness	4.5–5	
*Cleavage	one perfect, two good	
Fracture	uneven	
Habit	crystals tabular or short prisms; massive, compact or fibrous	
Twinning	common	
Specific gravity	2.8–3.1	
*Other tests	dissolves in hydrochloric acid depositing silica	
Crystal system	triclinic	
*Occurrence	in thermally metamorphosed limestones at igneous contacts, often associated with calcium-rich garnets	

and diopside; the silica may have been introduced from the igneous rocks

Examples wollastonite in the Black Forest (Germany), Brittany (France), Csiklowa (Romania), Crestmore, California (USA) and Pargos (Finland); rhodonite at Broken Hill, NSW (Australia), Sverdlovsk, the Urals (USSR) and Langban (Sweden)

Anthophyllite $(Mg,Fe)_7Si_8O_{22}(OH)_2$

Anthophyllite belongs to the amphibole group – an important group of rock-forming silicates in igneous and metamorphic rocks. Amphiboles are hydrous minerals and they break down by losing water during high-temperature metamorphism. Also belonging to the amphibole group is the mineral cummingtonite $((Mg,Fe)_7Si_8O_{22}(OH)_2)$. Though not forming a distinct chemical series, anthophyllite and cummingtonite are so alike that mineralogists can identify them only by detailed optical or X-ray tests. Cummingtonite forms a chemical series with *grunerite*, which is the iron-rich member. The aluminium-rich variety of anthophyllite is called *gedrite*. Asbestos-grade anthophyllite is called *amosite*.

Anthophyllite

Aggregate of fibrous anthophyllite

Cummingtonite

	ANTHOPHYLLITE
**Colour	white, grey, green, brown (anthophyllite) brown (cummingtonite)
Lustre	vitreous, silky when fibrous
Transparency	translucent
Hardness	5–6
Cleavage	prismatic, perfect
Fracture	uneven
Habit	usually fibrous aggregates; crystals rare
Twinning	common in cummingtonite
Specific gravity	2.8–3.4 (anthophyllite); 3.2–3.6 (cummingtonite)
Crystal system	orthorhombic (anthophyllite); monoclinic (cummingtonite)
Occurrence	anthophyllite is a metamorphic mineral of magnesium-rich sediments associated with cordierite; cummingtonite is a metamorphic mineral of regionally metamorphosed basic igneous rocks and some hornfelses
Examples	anthophyllite at Kongsberg (Norway), Fahlan (Sweden), Orijarvi (Finland); cummingtonite at Cummington, Massachusetts (USA) and Orijarvi (Finland); grunerite in the iron deposits of Lake Superior (USA)

$Ca_2(Mg,Fe)_5Si_8O_{22}(OH,F)_2$ # Tremolite-Actinolite

Tremolite and actinolite are amphiboles that form a chemical series. Tremolite contains little or no iron and is almost colourless. The iron content in actinolite produces a green colour, the most attractive variety being *nephrite*, or *greenstone*, the more common form of jade. Nephrite is tough and takes a good polish. Beautiful nephrites in New Zealand are called Maori stone, because of their widespread use in ancient Maori art. Tremolite and actinolite often occur in fibrous masses. They were the first such materials to be called asbestos. Fibrous tremolite is used for insulating and fire-proofing. They both occur in relatively low-grade metamorphic rocks. Actinolite is characteristic of the greenschist facies. Tremolite was discovered in Tremola, a valley in the Alps.

Actinolite

Tremolite

Nephrite

Asbestos

	TREMOLITE-ACTINOLITE
*Colour	white or grey (tremolite) to dark green (actinolite)
Lustre	vitreous, silky when fibrous
Transparency	transparent to translucent
Hardness	5–6
Cleavage	prismatic, good, (120° cleavage angle)
Fracture	uneven
*Habit	long bladed or prismatic crystals; massive or fibrous
Twinning	common
Specific gravity	3–3.4
Crystal system	monoclinic
Alteration	to talc (tremolite); to chlorite, epidote, serpentine and calcite (actinolite)
Occurrence	characteristic of thermally metamorphosed magnesian limestones associated with dolomite, calcite, diopside, forsterite and quartz; in altered ultrabasic rocks associated with talc; actinolite occurs in some schists associated with albite, chlorite and epidote, especially metabasic rocks
Examples	tremolite at Campolongo and Val Tremola (Switzerland), Edwards and Balmat, New York (USA) and the Urals (USSR); actinolite at the Zillertal (Austria) and Val Malenco (Italy); nephrite in central Asia especially the Bogotol Mountains (USSR)

Hornblende $(Ca,Na)_{2-3}(Mg,Fe,Al)_5(Si,Al)_8O_{22}(OH)_2$

Hornblende is an amphibole whose composition varies widely. This gives rise to a number of varieties. *Edenite* is a pale green hornblende, poor in iron, while *pargasite* is a dark green or bluish green type, rich in iron. *Basaltic hornblende*, which occurs in iron-rich basic igneous rocks, contains titanium and sodium and is brown or black. Like other amphiboles, hornblende is distinguished from pyroxenes, which are often similar in appearance, by having two cleavages at an angle of 120°. Hornblende is a widespread and abundant rock-forming mineral. It is characteristic of medium-grade metabasic rocks known as amphibolites. It is a common consitutent of syenites and diorites. The name is derived from the German words meaning 'horn' and 'to blind', in reference to its lustre.

Hornblende

Hornblende

two cleavages intersecting at 120°

Hornblende with red garnet

	HORNBLENDE	
*Colour	light green to dark green (almost black)	
Lustre	vitreous	
Transparency	translucent to nearly opaque	
Streak	white to grey	
Hardness	5−6	
*Cleavage	prismatic, good (120° cleavage angle)	
Fracture	uneven	
Habit	long or short prismatic crystals, massive, granular or fibrous	
Twinning	common	
Specific gravity	3−3.5	
Crystal system	monoclinic	
Occurrence	very widespread in igneous rocks especially intermediate and acid types; major mineral in metamorphosed basic rocks; uncommon in metamorphosed dolomites and ironstones	
Examples	Edenville, New York (USA), Pargas and Pernio (Finland), Hurry Inlet (Greenland) and Ontario (Canada)	

$Na_2(Mg,Fe,Al)_5Si_8O_{22}(OH)_2$ # Glaucophane-Riebeckite

The glaucophane-riebeckite series of amphiboles have characteristic colours, the deeper shades of riebeckite reflecting its higher iron content. Fibrous riebeckite, called *crocidolite* or *blue asbestos*, has been mined in South Africa and elsewhere for insulating material. It is now regarded as harmful, crocidolite being a greater health hazard than crystotile asbestos. A related blue-green mineral *arfvedsonite* is found in highly alkaline syenites and associated pegmatites. *Tiger's eye* is a silicified form of crocidolite which has been weathered to yellow and brown. Glaucophane is the essential amphibole in blueschists, which are metamorphosed sediments formed at high pressure and low temperature. Riebeckite occurs in alkaline igneous rocks, particularly alkali granites.

Crocidolite

Riebeckite

Glaucophane

	GLAUCOPHANE-RIEBECKITE
*Colour	grey, grey-blue or lavender blue (glaucophane); dark blue or black (riebeckite)
Lustre	vitreous, silky when fibrous
Transparency	translucent
Streak	white to light blue
Hardness	5–6
Cleavage	prismatic, good
Fracture	uneven
Habit	prismatic or acicular crystals, rare; common as fibrous aggregates
Twinning	common
Specific gravity	3–3.4
Crystal system	monoclinic
Occurrence	glaucophane is a metamorphic mineral found in schists derived from greywackes and clays via low-temperature, high-pressure metamorphism; riebeckite in soda trachytes, rhyolites and granites
Examples	glaucophane as crystals in schists at Piedmont (Italy); as fibrous aggregates in California (USA), Groix Island (France), Svalbard (Norway) and western Alps; riebeckite as crystals in granite at Quincy, Massachusetts (USA) and in schists in Galicia (Spain); crocidolite in South Africa, Australia and . Brazil

Muscovite $KAl_2(AlSi_3O_{10})(OH,F)_2$

Muscovite is a widespread member of the mica group of minerals. It is best known as a mostly colourless, flaky mineral which can form enormous crystals, up to 9–15 m² (100–160 sq ft), in some pegmatites. The first window panes were made of muscovite and it is still used in oil stoves and lamps, because it resists heat. Varieties include *sericite*, a fine-grained white mica, *illite*, a degraded white mica found in soils, *paragonite*, a sodium-containing variety found rarely in some schists, and *glauconite*, a green mineral which is found in greensands. An allied lithium-containing mineral *lepidolite* is an attractive pink.

basal cleavage surface

Muscovite

Muscovite

Crystals

cleavage

Mica pegmatite

books of mica

	MUSCOVITE	
*Colour	colourless or pale grey, green or brown	
Lustre	vitreous, pearly parallel to cleavage	
Transparency	transparent to translucent	
*Hardness	2–2.5	
*Cleavage	basal, perfect; cleavage flakes flexible and elastic	
Habit	crystals tabular and hexagonal in outline; foliated masses or 'books'; small scales and plates	
Twinning	common	
Specific gravity	2.8–2.9	
Crystal system	monoclinic (pseudo-hexagonal)	
Alteration	very resistant to weathering	
Occurrence	widespread in low temperature granites	
Examples	alongside biotite; in greisens and especially in pegmatites as large crystals; abundant in schists and gneisses; it is a common detrital mineral resistant to weathering and easily moved by water due to its lightness and flaky form in pegmatites in Ontario (Canada), New Hampshire and South Dakota (USA), throughout the Alps, Bihar and Madras (India) and in Brazil	

$K(Mg,Fe)_3AlSi_3O_{10}(OH,F)_2$ **Biotite-Phlogopite**

hese micas form a series ranging from ark, iron-rich biotites to the pale hlogopite ($KMg_3AlSi_3O_{10}(OH,F)_2$). hlogopite has a higher resistance to eat than muscovite and has similar ses. Like muscovite, these micas can ccur as huge crystals up to 2 m (6.6 ft) diameter. Biotite often forms the ark mineral in granites. Its crystal rm as small scales and plates istinguishes it from hornblende. The lignment of biotite crystals, alongside ose of chlorite and muscovite, often ves metamorphic rocks their haracteristic fabric.

basal cleavage

Biotite

Pseudohexagonal crystal of biotite

Vermiculite

	BIOTITE-PHLOGOPITE
*Colour	phlogopite is golden brown, often coppery; biotite is dark green-brown or black
Lustre	vitreous or pearly in phlogopite, submetallic, splendent in biotite
Transparency	transparent to translucent
*Hardness	2.5 – 3
*Cleavage	basal, perfect
Habit	tabular, pseudo-hexagonal crystals, lamellar aggregates or disseminated flakes
Twinning	common
Specific gravity	2.7 – 3.3 (increasing with iron content)
Crystal system	monoclinic (pseudo-hexagonal)
Occurrence	phlogopite in marbles produced by metamorphism of siliceous dolomitic limestones; magnesium-rich biotites in mica-periodotites and kimberlite; biotite widespread in granite, syenite and diorite and fine-grained equivalents; biotite occurs in many schists and gneisses
Examples	large biotites in pegmatites in the Ilmen Mountains (USSR), Greenland, Scandinavia and Brazil; phlogopite at Campolongo (Switzerland), Pargas (Finland), Ontario (Canada) and Sri Lanka

Chlorite $(Mg,Fe,Al)_6(Si,Al)_4O_{10}(OH)_8$

Chlorite is the name of a group of minerals related to the micas, but which do not contain any sodium or potassium. One variety *clinochore* occurs as monoclinic tabular crystals. *Penninite* occurs as pseudo-hexagonal crystals which can be very large. Fine examples occur in Zermatt, Switzerland, and Zillertal, Austria. The variety *ripidolite* usually occurs in scaly masses or in radiating or tubular form. Chlorite is an abundant mineral in many low-grade metamorphic rocks, such as chlorite-schists and chlorite-phyllites. In low- to medium-grade, regionally metamorphosed rocks, chlorite may be associated with the mineral chloritoid. The latter bears a superficial resemblance to chlorite, from which it is named, but differs in composition. Chlorite may be distinguished from chloritoid by its flexible, but inelastic flakes (flakes of chloritoid are brittle) and a much lower hardness (2–2.5 against 6.5). Because chlorite has a varied chemical composition and is stable at low-temperatures it occurs in a wide variety of rock types formed at low temperatures. The name chlorite comes from the Greek *khloros*, which means 'yellow-green'. This describes the mineral's typical colour.

Ripidolite

Chlorite

	CHLORITE	
*Colour	mainly pale or bright green	
Lustre	pearly	
Transparency	translucent to opaque	
*Hardness	2–2.5	
*Cleavage	perfect basal, giving flexible flakes	
Habit	six-sided tabular crystals; foliated masses or scales, often radiating fan-shapes	
Twinning	common	
Specific gravity	2.6–3.3	
Other tests	greasy feel when in flakes	
Crystal system	monoclinic	
Occurrence	widespread as late-stage mineral or secondary product in vesicles and veins in igneous rocks; alteration product of ferromagnesian minerals and volcanic glasses; weathering and diagenetic product in sediments, especially greywackes; in low-grade phyllites and schists	
Examples		Amity, New York (USA), Achmatovsk, the Urals (USSR), Zermatt (Switzerland), Markt Leugast, Bavaria (Germany) and Zillertal (Austria)

$Mg_3Si_2O_5(OH)_4$ Serpentine

Serpentine is the name for a group of common secondary minerals. The group includes *chrysotile*, a type of asbestos that forms fibrous yellow-white or green aggregates with a silky lustre, *lizardite*, a compact, whitish variety made up of tiny plates, and *antigorite*, which is lamellar and occurs as tough, compact, dark green masses. Serpentine minerals are formed by low-temperature hydration of ultramafic rocks, including dunite and pyroxenite. Coloured varieties are used for ornaments and internal decorations, because their low hardness makes them easy to work. The name refers to the snake-like appearance of the massive form.

Yellow serpentine

Chrysotile

Green serpentine

fibrous serpentine

	SERPENTINE	
*Colour	pale to dark green, may be stained dull red	
*Lustre	silky to waxy or dull	
Transparency	opaque, occasionally translucent	
Hardness	2.5 – 3.5	
Cleavage	perfect basal in flaky varieties	
Fracture	conchoidal or splintery	
Habit	chrysotile forms small veins with fibres at right angles to the walls; lizardite is compact; antigorite in flakes	
Specific gravity	2.5 – 2.6	
*Other tests	sometimes has a soapy feel	
Crystal system	monoclinic or orthorhombic	
Occurrence	widespread; mostly as large rock bodies formed by hydrothermal alteration of the ultramafic rocks dunite and pyroxenite; it may surround unaltered rocks; associated minerals are talc, magnesite, dolomite and chromite	
Examples	Troodos Mountains (Cyprus), the Lizard, Cornwall (England), Saxony (Germany) and many locations in the USA	

Talc $Mg_3Si_4O_{10}(OH)_2$

Talc is the softest mineral in Mohs' scale of hardness, on which it is listed as number 1. The massive variety *steatite*, also called *soapstone* because of its greasy feel, is an attractive, easily worked form used for ornaments. French chalk is a variety of steatite. Talc has uses as a dry lubricant, as a filler in such substances as paints, paper and rubber, in cosmetics, and as an electrical and thermal insulator. Cooking vessels are made from soapstone. An allied mineral *pyrophyllite* $((Al_2Si_4O_{10}(OH)_2)$ has similar properties and uses as talc.

Steatite

Foliated mass

Crystalline talc

pearly lustre

	TALC	
*Colour	white, grey or pale green	
Lustre	dull, pearly on cleavages	
Transparency	translucent	
*Hardness	1	
Cleavage	basal perfect	
Habit	foliated masses, sometimes in radiating groups; granular or compact	
Specific gravity	2.6 – 2.8	
*Other tests	soapy feel	
Crystal system	monoclinic	
Occurrence	forms as a secondary mineral by the alteration of olivine, pyroxene and amphibole and often accompanies serpentine in veins and faults in magnesium-rich rocks; sometimes formed by low-grade metamorphism of dolomitic limestones	
Examples	Styria (Austria), Madras (India), Transvaal (South Africa), the Pyrenees, Korea and a number of places in the USA, Canada and USSR	

This widely distributed form of silica is used in jewellery and for ornaments. There are several attractive varieties. *Rock crystal* is water-clear. *Milky quartz* is white. Colours are caused by impurities, such as ferric oxide in violet *amethyst*, manganese or titanium in *rose quartz*, and iron hydrates in yellow *citrine*. *Tiger's eye* is formed by fibrous inclusions of crocidolite. Tiny tourmaline, rutile and zoisite inclusions give *blue quartz*. *Rutilated quartz* contains needle-like yellow and red rutile crystals. *Aventurine quartz* contains scales of mica or goethite, giving a spangled green or brown look. Quartz is used in glass-making, ceramics, refractories, building materials and abrasives. Its piezoelectric property makes it useful in pressure-sensitive devices.

Rose quartz

Rock crystal

Smoky quartz

Citrine

	QUARTZ	
Colour	colourless or white with a wide range of tints	igneous and metamorphic rocks, and in most clastic sediments; a common gangue mineral in veins and cavity fillings, where most good crystals specimens are found
*Lustre	vitreous	
Transparency	transparent to translucent	
*Hardness	7	
Cleavage	none	
*Fracture	conchoidal	**Examples**
*Habit	crystals usually six-sided prisms terminated by six faces; prism faces horizontally striated	ubiquitous; rock crystals at Minas Gerais (Brazil), the Dauphiné (France), St. Gotthard (Switzerland); smoky quartz in the Cairngorms (Scotland), and the Alps; citrine, rose quartz and amethyst at Minas Gerais (Brazil), aventurine quartz at Meteor Crater, Arizona (USA), San Cristobal (Mexico) and Rhineland (Germany)
Twinning	very common but usually unobservable in hand specimen	
Specific gravity	2.6	
Crystal system	trigonal	
Alteration	very stable to weathering	
Occurrence	commonest mineral on the Earth's surface; in many acid	

Chalcedony SiO_2

Chalcedony, the compact form of silica, is composed of microscopic quartz crystals. It is softer than quartz and denser than opal. The main types are *chalcedony*, which is uniformly coloured, and *agate*, which has curved bands or zones of varying colour. Chalcedony is a popular ornamental or gemstone. Varieties include the red to reddish brown, translucent *carnelian*, the red, opaque *jasper*, the apple-green *chrysoprase*, and *heliotrope*, which is green with red spots. *Flint* and *chert* are impure forms of chalcedony. *Onyx* is a variety of agate, with parallel layers of black and white. Chalcedony occurs in some fossils, such as petrified wood.

Agate

Stalactitic form

Botryoidal form

	CHALCEDONY
Colour	variable, white to black via grey, red or brown shades
Lustre	waxy to vitreous
Transparency	transparent to substranslucent
Hardness	6.5
Cleavage	none
Fracture	conchoidal
***Habit**	mostly botryoidal or stalactitic, often banded; lines cavities; massive or nodular
***Specific gravity**	about 2.6
Crystal system	none (cryptocrystalline)
***Occurrence**	veins, cavity linings and masses in many different rock types; flint forms mainly in limestones
Examples	agate in Rio Grande do Sul (Brazil) and Idar-Oberstein (Germany); carnelian in Brazil, Uraguay and California (USA); chrysoprase in Queensland (Australia), the Urals (USSR) and California (USA); flint in the chalk of SE England (e.g. the white cliffs of Dover)

Opal is hydrated silica – that is, it contains about one-tenth (and sometimes as much as one-third) water. Opal is never crystalline, but it displays a rich play of colours, or 'fire', caused by the internal refraction of light by the arrays of tiny spheres of amorphous silica that make up the mineral. *Black opal*, which was once more precious than diamond, and the reddish *fire opal* are the most prized varieties. *Hydrophane* is a variety that becomes transparent when immersed in water. *Geyserite*, or *siliceous sinter*, is an opal deposited by hot springs and geysers. Opal forms the skeletons of some marine organisms, such as diatoms. *Diatomite* or *diatomaceous earth* is a sedimentary rock made up of the remains of diatoms.

Opal showing play of colours

Liver opal

Fossil opalized wood

Milk opal

	OPAL	
Colour	variable; white, yellow, red, brown and others usually of pale shades	
***Lustre**	waxy or resinous	
Transparency	transparent to subtranslucent	
Hardness	5.5–6.5	
Cleavage	none	
Fracture	conchoidal	
***Habit**	massive, often stalactitic or rounded forms	
Specific gravity	1.8–2.3	
Crystal system	none, one of the few amorphous minerals	
Occurrence	formed by weathering and alteration of siliceous rocks being deposited at low temperatures, especially in the area of geysers and hot springs; forms the skeletons of diatoms, radiolaria and sponges	
Examples	in altered trachyte in Czechoslovakia and in sandstones of White Cliffs, NSW (Australia); fire opal at Queretaro (Mexico) and variously coloured in Transylvania (Romania); wood opal in Yellowstone National Park, Wyoming (USA) and Lake Omodeo (Sardinia)	

Alkali Feldspars $KAlSi_3O_8$

Sanidine, *orthoclase* and *microcline* are forms of alkali (or potassium) feldspars formed, respectively, at high, medium-to-high, and low temperatures. It is difficult to distinguish between orthoclase and microcline except when they are coloured. *Amazonite* is a green gem variety of microcline, while orthoclase often occurs as pink to red phenocrysts in granites. *Perthite* is an alkali feldspar, containing undulating layers of albite (a plagioclase feldspar) within individual crystals. The opposite phenomena of alkali feldspar lamellae in albite crystals are called *antiperthites*. *Adularia* is a colourless or white variety of orthoclase commonly found in pseudo-orthorhombic crystals. Some show an opalescent, white or blue play of colour. These are known as 'moonstones' and are used as gemstones. The alkali feldspars are important rock-forming minerals.

White microcline

Orthoclase with tourmaline and quartz

Orthoclase crystal

Amazonstone

	ALKALI FELDSPARS (POTASSIUM FELDSPARS)		
*Colour	sanidine, colourless to grey; orthoclase white to pink; microcline colourless to grey, sometimes green	**Crystal system**	sanidine and orthoclase are monoclinic, microcline is triclinic
Lustre	vitreous, pearly parallel to cleavage	**Occurrence**	sanidine forms phenocrysts in volcanic rocks and occurs in high-temperature metamorphic rocks; orthoclase is the commonest alkali feldspar of most igneous and metamorphic rocks; microcline occurs in granites, schists and gneisses and as grains in sedimentary rocks
Transparency	sanidine, transparent; orthoclase and microcline, transparent to translucent		
*Hardness	6–6.5		
*Cleavage	two perfect		
Fracture	conchoidal to uneven		
*Habit	sanidine, tabular or prismatic crystals; orthoclase and microcline, prismatic, may be of square cross-section	**Examples**	Carlsbad (Czechoslovakia) for orthoclase; Pantellevia (Sicily) and Cap d'Entola (Elba) for sanidine; Pikes Peak, Colorado (USA) for amazonite
Twinning	common		
Specific gravity	2.5–2.6		

Plagioclase feldspars form a continuous series ranging from *albite* ($NaAlSi_3O_8$) through *oligoclase, andesine, labradorite* and *bytownite* to *anorthite* ($CaAl_2Si_2O_8$). Precise classification is generally not possible in hand specimens. Plagioclase feldspars are distinguished from alkali feldspars by striations on the cleavage surfaces caused by the intersection of lamellar twins with the cleavage surfaces. *Sunstone*, a gem variety of oligoclase, is usually reddish-brown or reddish-orange, with a glitter effect caused by aligned inclusions of iron minerals. Labradorite shows a beautiful play of colours. Like alkali feldspars, plagioclase feldspars are important rock-forming minerals.

Oligoclase crystal

Albite crystal

Labradorite

PLAGIOCLASE		
Colour	white, greyish, pinkish or greenish; dark grey or blue-grey in some labradorites	
Lustre	vitreous	
Transparency	transparent to translucent	
*Hardness	6–6.5	
Cleavage	two good cleavages	
Fracture	uneven	
Habit	prismatic or tabular crystals; also massive, granular	
*Twinning	repeated and simple twinning common and may occur together	
Specific gravity	2.6–2.8	
Other tests	labradorite often shows a play of blues and greens on cleavage surfaces	
Crystal system	triclinic	
Alteration	albite to kaolinite clay, more calcic minerals to a mixture of zoisite, calcite and albite	
Occurrence	widely distributed; in many igneous rocks, sodic plagioclase in granite and calcic plagioclase in basalt and gabbro; albite in pegmatite and spilitic lavas	
Examples	labradorite in anorthosites in Norway, Labrador (Canada) and the USSR, fine specimens known as *spectrolite* in Finland; sunstone in pegmatites in Norway, Canada and the USSR	

Nepheline $NaAlSiO_4$

Nepheline is a common feldspathoid mineral. (Feldspathoids are a group of rock-forming aluminosilicates similar to feldspars, but containing less silica.) It never occurs as a primary mineral associated with quartz in igneous rocks. The name nepheline comes from the Greek word for 'cloud', an allusion to the cloudiness observed when nepheline is placed in acid. Nepheline usually contains about 25 per cent of the 'potassium nepheline' *kalsilite* ($KAlSiO_4$) with which it forms a partial series. Kalsilite itself is very rare, being known only in some lavas on the Uganda-Zaire border. *Elaeolite* is a course-grained or massive, greenish, brownish or reddish nepheline with a greasy lustre. An associated mineral, *cancrinite*, is much less common. It tends to be yellow, yellow-brown or green and is rarely crystalline. Like nepheline, it is usually massive or occurs as grains. Nepheline is used in glass, ceramics and in the textile and oil industries. It is a minor ore of aluminium.

White crystals

Massive form

vitreous lustre

	NEPHELINE
Colour	usually colourless, white or grey, sometimes greenish or brown
Lustre	vitreous to greasy
Transparency	transparent to translucent
Hardness	6
Cleavage	poor
Fracture	conchoidal
Habit	rarely in six-sided prismatic crystals, usually massive
Specific gravity	2.6 – 2.7
*Other tests	gelatinizes in hydrochloric acid
Crystal system	hexagonal
Alteration	to white mica flakes; may alter to orange-red colours
Occurrence	in silica-poor igneous rocks, such as nepheline-syenites and phonolites (as an essential constituent mineral); rare basic volcanic rocks composed of nepheline and pyroxene are called nephelite, their intrusive equivalents are called ijolite
Examples	Kola Peninsula (USSR), Oslo District (Norway), Bancroft (Canada), Litchfield, Maine and Magnet Cove, Arkansas (USA), Julianehaals district (S Greenland) and East Africa

Leucite is a member of the feldspathoid group of minerals. It is unstable under high pressures and does not occur in rocks that form underground by slow cooling. Hence, it appears only in lavas. The large crystals found in the lavas of Mount Vesuvius are a well-known example. The presence of feldspathoids such as leucite in an igneous rock precludes the presence of quartz. Thus these minerals form the basis of the classification of silica-poor rocks. The oval pinkish or white spots in some syenite rocks are thought to be 'pseudoleucites' – that is, the original leucite has changed to potassium feldspar and nepheline. Analcime and garnet share with leucite the perfect icositetrahedral crystal shape. But unlike leucite, analcime typically occurs in cavities, while garnet is not white or grey. Leucite has no real economic value although it has been used in the past as a source of potassium for fertilisers. The name comes from the Greek word for 'white'.

Crystals in volcanic rock

Icositetrahedral crystal in volcanic rock

	LEUCITE
Colour	white or ash-grey
Lustre	vitreous
Transparency	translucent
Streak	white
Hardness	5.5 – 6
Cleavage	very poor
Fracture	conchoidal
*Habit	perfect trapezohedral (icositetrahedral) crystals; cubic aspect inherited from high-temperature crystallization
Twinning	very common, causing striations on crystal faces
Specific gravity	2.5
Crystal system	tetragonal below 625°C (1157°F), cubic above
Alteration	to a mixture of orthoclase and nepheline

*Occurrence	only found in volcanic rocks and never in association with quartz; typically in potassium-rich, silica-poor lavas, such as trachytes
Examples	Mount Vesuvius and area around Rome (Italy), Bfumbira volcanic field (Uganda), Zaire, Eifel district (Germany), Leucite Hills, Wyoming (USA)

Sodalite $Na_8Al_6Si_6O_{24}Cl_2$

Sodalite occurs with other feldspathoids in silica-poor igneous rocks. Its blue forms are the best known. Also part of the sodalite group are *nosean* or *noselite* ($Na_8Al_6Si_6O_{24}(SO_4)$), and a calcium-containing type of nosean called *haüyne*. Both occur in alkali-rich volcanic rocks, such as phonolite. A better known related mineral is *lazurite* ($(Na,Ca)_8(Al,Si)_{12}O_{24}(S,SO_4)$). Lazurite is a major constituent of lapis lazuli, which contains, alongside other associated minerals, small inclusions of pyrite. These inclusions not only make the rock attractive and valuable, but they also help to distinguish lazurite from blue sodalite.

Lapis lazuli

Sodalite

Haüyne in volcanic rock

	SODALITE
*Colour	often blue, also white, pink or yellow
Lustre	vitreous or greasy
Transparency	transparent to translucent
Streak	white
Hardness	5.5–6
Cleavage	dodecahedral, poor
Fracture	conchoidal to uneven
Habit	crystals rare in dodecahedra; commonly massive, granular
Specific gravity	2.3
*Other tests	reddish fluorescence in ultraviolet light
Crystal system	cubic
*Occurrence	with nepheline and cancrinite in alkaline igneous rocks, such as nepheline syenites, and in some silica-poor lavas and dyke rocks

Examples ditroite, a sodalite syenite from Ditrău (Romania) is a well-known example; others at Bancroft, Ontario and Ice River, British Columbia (Canada), Litchfield, Maine and Magnet Cove, Arkansas (USA) and Vesuvius (Italy)

$NaAlSi_2O_6.H_2O$ Analcime

Analcime or analcite is one of a family of alumino-silicate minerals called zeolites. These minerals contain water molecules in spaces within the framework crystal lattice. The water may be expelled on heating. The name zeolite comes from the Greek words meaning 'to boil' and 'stone'. It refers to the fact that zeolites froth or boil when heated. Zeolites have many uses in industry, for example as catalysts and drying agents. Zeolites occur as low-grade metamorphic minerals, and also in vesicles (small cavities) in lavas, or in shallow igneous intrusions. Chemically and in crystal form and structure, analcime is closely related to leucite. It is distinguished by occurrence, as leucite is always embedded in the rock matrix. It is named after the Greek *analkes*, meaning 'weak', because of its weak pyroelectric properties when heated or rubbed.

Icositetrahedral crystals

Crystals in basalt

vesicles

Aggregate of crystals

	ANALCIME		
Colour	colourless, white or grey, may be tinted with yellow, green or pink		heated, becomes slightly charged
Lustre	vitreous	**Crystal system**	cubic
Transparency	transparent to nearly opaque	***Occurrence**	in cavities in basalt and dolerite affected by low temperature hydration and alteration, associated with other zeolites, calcite or prehnite; it may form in the early stages of metamorphism of volcanic glass in tuffaceous sandstones; a primary constituent of feldspathoidal basalts
Streak	white		
Hardness	5–5.5		
Cleavage	imperfect, cubic		
Fracture	uneven to conchoidal; brittle		
Habit	usually in icositetrahedral crystals (as leucite), may be combined with cube		
Specific gravity	2.2–2.4		
Other tests	fuses to a colourless glass, colouring the flame yellow; decomposes in hydrochloric acid with the separation of silica; when rubbed or	**Examples**	Cyclopean Islands (Sicily), Tyrol (Austria), Iceland, Bergen Hill, New Jersey and Table Mountain, Colorado (USA)

Chabazite $CaAl_2Si_4O_{12}.6H_2O$

Chabazite is a member of the zeolite family (see analcime). Like other zeolites, it occurs in vesicles, joints, cracks and fissures in basalts and other lavas. Chabazite and other zeolites are widely used to indicate temperature and depth of burial in ocean-floor basalts of the zeolite facies. Its rhombohedral crystals are an aid to identification. It can be distinguished from calcite by its poorer cleavage and because it does not effervesce in dilute hydrochloric acid. A variety of chabazite, called *phacolite*, occurs as colourless lenticular crystals produced by twinning. Chabazite is named from the Greek word for 'hailstone', which it resembles.

Red-brown, rhombohedral crystals

White crystals in basalt

White crystals

	CHABAZITE	**Crystal system**	trigonal
Colour	colourless, white, flesh pink, yellowish or brown	**Occurrence**	in cavities and fissures in basalts, with other zeolites; also formed by chemical deposition from thermal waters
Lustre	vitreous		
Transparency	transparent to translucent		
Streak	white		
Hardness	4–5	**Examples**	good crystals are found in Bolzano (Italy), the Cyclopean Islands (Sicily), and in cavities in granites at Elba (Italy); other well-known localities include the Faeroe Islands (North Atlantic), Aussig (Bohemia), Idar Oberstein (Germany), Nova Scotia (Canada) and Patterson, New Jersey (USA)
Cleavage	rhombohedral, imperfect		
Fracture	uneven		
*Habit	usually in cube-like rhombohedral crystals; crystals may be complex or twinned; also in compact masses		
Twinning	common, interpenetrant		
Specific gravity	2.1–2.2		
Other tests	fuses to a nearly opaque whitish blebby glass; dissolves in hydrochloric acid with separation of silica		

Stilbite is a member of the zeolite family of minerals. The structure of the zeolites is such that structural ions may be replaced by the ions dissolved in the surrounding water. Thus the sodium ions in a sodium zeolite may be exchanged for the calcium in hard water. It typically occurs in cavities in basalts, often with another zeolite called *heulandite*. But while heulandite occurs in tabular crystals, twinned crystals of stilbite occur in a distinctive, sheaf-like form. Another distinguishing feature of both stilbite and heulandite is their lustre, which is pearly parallel to the cleavage, but vitreous elsewhere.

Light brown crystals in basalt

Radiating acicular crystals

Pink crystal aggregate

	STILBITE		
Colour	white, sometimes yellowish or pink, may be brick-red	**Crystal system**	monoclinic
*Lustre	vitreous, pearly on cleavage surfaces	**Occurrence**	in cavities in amygdaloidal basalts, often with heulandite and calcite; also in granites, schists and ore deposits; also found in the early stages of metamorphism of tuffaceous sandstones
Transparency	transparent to translucent		
Streak	white		
Hardness	3.5 – 4		
Cleavage	one perfect cleavage		
Fracture	uneven		
*Habit	as sheaf-like aggregates of twinned crystals, also as radial or globular aggregates	**Examples**	good crystals at Patterson, New Jersey (USA), Kilpatrick and Isle of Skye (Scotland), Nova Scotia (Canada), Rio Grande do Sul (Brazil) and at Teigarhorn (Iceland); also found in granites at Baveno, and in Elba (Italy), Tyrol (Austria), Sweden, Deccan Traps (India) and in the Lake Superior copper district (USA)
Twinning	common, giving cruciform, interpenetrant twins		
Specific gravity	2.1 – 2.2		
Other tests	soluble in hydrochloric acid, and fuses easily to an opaque white glass		

Granites

Granites are coarse-grained rocks with a mottled appearance. They comprise a mixture of glassy quartz, white, pink or red alkali feldspar, minor amounts of dark minerals, and often white, sodic plagioclase. Their low density and resistance to weathering means that they usually form high, rugged terrains. Quarrymen use the term granite for almost any hard rock. Geologists use it either in a restricted sense, or as a blanket term for granitoids of acid or intermediate composition. Their complex and varied origins give rise to a great variety of types. Weather-resistant stones are polished for use as decorative facings on buildings. Granites that weather to pure kaolin provide china clay.

Biotite granite

Graphic granite

Hornblende biotite granite

phenocrysts of alkali feldspar

Porphyritic granite

xenolith of basic rock

	GRANITES		
Colour	colourless grains, also mottled in white, pink or red, some grey or dark grains		into which well-formed crystals project; may be associated with much late-stage mineralization
Colour index	5–20	**Classification**	acid plutonic igneous rock QAPF field 3 (and 2 – alkali feldspar granite)
Mineralogy	essential quartz, alkali feldspar and plagioclase in variable amounts, usually with hornblende and/or biotite; muscovite may occur	**Alteration**	usually quite resistant to weathering, but can give clay minerals and quartz sand; can show hydrothermal or pneumatolytic alteration
Texture	coarse to very coarse-grained; usually granular; may be porphyritic with well-shaped phenocrysts of feldspar; sometimes foliated; coarse intergrowths of quartz and feldspars can form a 'graphic' texture	**Occurrence**	intrusive, most commonly occurring in batholiths
Structure	commonly contain xenoliths, may contain cavities (druses)	**Examples**	SW England, Galloway (Scotland), tin-belt of Southeast Asia, coastal batholith (Peru); E Greenland, New England batholith (Australia)

Granodiorite

Granodiorite is a coarse-grained intrusive igneous rock. It is similar to granite in composition, but contains less alkali feldspar. As a result, it does not usually show the reddish colour of some granites, even when weathered, but is normally greyish white. It is the most common igneous rock, occurring as plutons in mountain-building regions, where it is often associated with other igneous rock types, such as diorite or granite. It also occurs in dykes. The US geologist George Becker was the first person to use the term on maps of the Gold Belt of the Sierra Nevada, California.

Granodiorite

Granodiorite

Granodiorite

	GRANODIORITE		
Colour	greyish white	**Occurrence**	the most voluminous of all plutonic rocks, occurring in the same environments as granite; they form large areas within Precambrian gneissose massifs and plutons within orogenic belts; associated rocks are diorites, quartz diorites and sometimes granites
Colour index	usually 5 – 25		
Mineralogy	essential quartz, plagioclase, and lesser amounts of alkali feldspar, with minor amounts of hornblende and biotite; may also contain pyroxene or muscovite		
Texture	coarse-grained; grains approximately of equal size (granular texture); mafic minerals may show some crystal faces (subhedral); occasionally porphyritic, phenocrysts of alkali feldspar; may show orbicular texture	**Examples**	Donegal (Ireland), Mountsorrel Intrusion, Charnwood Forest, Leicestershire (England); Caledonian mountain belt in Scandinavia and Cordilleran belt of western North America
Classification	intermediate plutonic igneous rock QAPF field 4		

Pegmatite

This distinctive rock is often light in colour and extremely coarse, though grain sizes vary greatly. Pegmatite bodies range in size from centimetres to thousands of metres. They occur widely in both stable areas and in younger continental mountain belts. Although commonly composed of the same minerals found in most igneous rocks, they may also contain rare minerals. They may be economically valuable as sources of mica, silica and gemstones, including emerald and topaz. Pegmatites also form a source for metals and raw materials used in the ceramic, electronic and nuclear power industries.

Pegmatite

Pegmatite   *mica*

Pegmatite

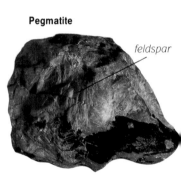

feldspar

PEGMATITE

Colour variable, depending on constituents

Mineralogy commonly quartz or alkali feldspar, but can be those of any igneous rock type; may contain less common minerals, such as beryl, topaz or tourmaline; apatite, beryl, garnet, magnetite, topaz and zircon sparse but widespread

Texture notable for very coarse grain-size, average 10 cm (4 in) but variable over short distances; mica and quartz crystals may be 1–3 m (3–10 ft) across, feldspar crystals (2–10 m) (6–33 ft); textures similar to those of common igneous rocks, but on a larger scale; often equi-granular with grains of irregular shape; also porphyritic; some bodies may be zoned; may contain cavities a few centimetres wide with beautifully formed crystals of gem quality

Examples Precambrian terrain of Fennoscandia, deposits with rare minerals at Varutrask (Sweden); pegmatitic pyroxenites at the base of the Merensky Reef, Bushveld Layered Complex (South Africa)

Dacite

Dacite is the volcanic equivalent of granodiorite and tonalite, two intrusive rocks. Geologists use the term dacite for rocks containing between 63 and 69 per cent silica, which comprise at least 10 per cent quartz, and plagioclase feldspar (An less than 70 per cent). They may also contain minor amounts of biotite, hornblende and pyroxene. Dacites, together with andesites, are the most characteristic, if not the most abundant, volcanic rocks that are formed by volcanic action in mountain-building regions. The lava is extremely viscous and tends to form steep-sided flows, often with platy jointing or a block-like structure. It may also form domes or occur as pyroclastic rocks.

Dacite

Dacite

Porphyritic dacite

	DACITE
Colour	medium grey
Colour index	less than 20
Mineralogy	quartz and sodic plagioclase with minor amounts of biotite and/or hornblende and/or pyroxene
Texture	often porphyritic, with phenocrysts of plagioclase, augite or hypersthene, or rarely olivine; may form glassy or highly vesiculated rocks
Structure	may show flow-banding, also found as ignimbrites
Classification	intermediate volcanic QAPF fields 4 and 5
Occurrence	more common in orogenic and continental settings than in oceanic regions, forming chains of composite volcanoes, may also occur as domes on the upper flanks of large, mature volcanoes; may be associated with earthquakes
Examples	found as islands and on the continental margins around the Pacific Ocean, Indonesia and the Lesser Antilles; ignimbrites in the Great Basin (USA), in plateau regions of Mexico and Central America; the northern margins of the Alpine System, especially the Carpathians and N Turkey

Rhyolite

Rhyolite, an acid volcanic rock, is the chemical equivalent of granite but with finer grains. Light in colour and in weight, it may resemble flint. It often shows a banding of colour or texture, known as *flow banding*. This is caused by the flow of the lava and is commonly contorted. Rhyolites may also show spherulitic texture – containing spherical bodies less than 0.5 cm (0.2 in) across. They contain radially arranged, needle-like crystals, often of quartz or feldspar. Rhyolite magma is stiffer and flows less easily than basalt lava. As a result, it only occasionally reaches the Earth's surface.

Rhyolite

Flow-banded rhyolite

Flow-banded rhyolite

	RHYOLITE
Colour	white, greenish, grey, brownish or reddish
Mineralogy	quartz, alkali feldspar and plagioclase (oligoclase or albite), also glass of equivalent composition; mafic minerals include augite, hypersthene, iron-rich olivine (fayalite), biotite, magnetite and ilmenite
Texture	fine-grained or glassy, may contain phenocrysts of quartz, alkali feldspar, hornblende or mica in a microcrystalline groundmass
Structure	flow-banding may occur; more glassy types may show irregular or spheroidal fractures (perlitic fractures); may develop spherulitic or vesicular texture, the vesicles sometimes being filled to form amygdales; commonly brecciated, the main constituent of volcanic ash
Classification	acid volcanic igneous rock QAPF field 3
Occurrence	as plugs in volcanic vents, or short, thick flows, or as domes up to hundreds of metres across; rhyolitic eruptions are associated with strato-volcanoes, and the rocks formed are usually confined to the vicinity of the parent volcano
Examples	Landmannalangar (Iceland); Jersey (Channel Islands)

Obsidian

Obsidian, a volcanic glass formed by rapid cooling, has the same composition as dacite or rhyolite, with less than 1 per cent water. It is typically black and glassy, with a *conchoidal* (shell-like) fracture. The black colour appears because of the way the embryonic crystals in the glass scatter the light. Obsidian may be red-brown due to the presence of iron, and greenish or grey due to the presence of tiny gas bubbles. Shattered fragments of obsidian have sharp edges and it was once used to make implements and weapons. Especially prized are such varieties as snow-flake obsidian, which contains small, grey spherulites, and the silky lustred obsidian of Mexico.

Obsidian

conchoidal fracture

Obsidian

Obsidian *vesicles*

vitreous lustre

	OBSIDIAN		
Colour	black, greenish black, grey or red-brown	**Alteration**	igneous rock hydrates to form perlite, a grey, pearly-lustred volcanic glass, which characteristically has an intricate network of concentric cracks resembling an onion
Mineralogy	mostly glassy, of equivalent composition to rhyolite or granite		
Texture	none; glassy, although may contain less than 1 per cent minute crystals (microlites); may contain minute crystals of quartz, feldspar, pyroxene or magnetite	**Occurrence**	not widely distributed, although the commonest of natural glasses; formed when acid or intermediate lava is cooled very rapidly; occurs as flows and dykes, often associated with rhyolite
Structure	glass may contain spherical bodies (spherulites) ranging from microscopic to over a metre; perlitic cracks may be present; may be spotted or show flow-banding; breaks with a conchoidal fracture	**Examples**	Yellowstone National Park, Wyoming (USA), Cumbria (England), Lipari Islands (Italy), Mount Hecla, (Iceland), Japan, Java
Classification	acid or intermediate volcanic		

Pitchstone

Pitchstone, a volcanic glass, is formed when dacitic or rhyolitic lava is rapidly chilled on or near the Earth's surface. It is black, brown or red, with a resinous lustre resembling that of pitch. It is similar to obsidian, but it contains more crystalline material. This may comprise quartz, alkali or plagioclase feldspar, or pyroxene phenocrysts. Pitchstone is of a duller appearance than obsidian, because it contains more water (between 4 and 10 per cent). The origin of the water is not understood. It also has an irregular, hackly fracture, unlike the conchoidal fracture of obsidian. Pitchstone occurs at the base of acid lava flows or it may form the margins of intrusive dykes and sills.

Pitchstone   *resinous lustre*

Pitchstone

Pitchstone   *phenocrysts*

	PITCHSTONE		
Colour	dark coloured, black brown or grey	**Classification**	acid or intermediate volcanic igneous rock
Mineralogy	mostly glassy, but crystalline material may be quartz, alkali or plagioclase feldspar, pyroxene; may also contain iron-rich olivine (fayalite)	**Occurrence**	as flows and dykes, commonly associated with rhyolites
Texture	glassy, but contains more crystalline material than obsidian; phenocrysts common, of quartz and feldspar or even light green pyroxene	**Examples**	Islands of Arran and Eigg (Scotland), Shropshire and Devon (England), Meissen (Germany), Pantelleria (Italy), Hlinik (Hungary), Lugano (Switzerland)
Structure	flow structure common (see obsidian); perlitic structure also occurs, caused by tension set up during contraction on cooling; breaks with an irregular fracture		

Pumice

Pumice is a pale grey, frothy volcanic glass, usually of acid composition, although it can also be intermediate or mafic. It is an extremely light, porous rock, containing 50 to 75 per cent gas. Some types are so light that they float in water. *Scoria* is a mafic glass, similar to pumice, but denser. The vesicles are larger and more spherical in form, giving it an open cellular structure. Pumice is used as an abrasive. When mixed with cement, it makes a useful, lightweight building material. Pumice and ash erupted from volcanoes is sometimes transported by wind for thousands of kilometres. The thin deposit of ash and pumice – called *tephra* – is useful in correlating different rocks of the same age.

vesicles

Pumice

Pumice breccia

Basaltic scoria

	PUMICE		
Colour	very light grey, or yellowish	**Occurrence**	usually formed during explosive volcanic eruptions, but may also form by quieter bubbling at the top of lava flows; it may be carried on the wind for thousands of kilometres from the source volcano
Mineralogy	glass, but with accessory crystals of various silicates (e.g. sanidine, oligoclase), quartz, biotite, zeolites and calcite		
Texture	highly vesicular; many protuberances and vacuoles, which make it very light		
Structure	vacuoles may be oriented due to flow; may occur as fragments less than 1 cm (0.4 in) across, often flattened, in ignimbrites; scoria has an open cellular structure	**Examples**	Lipari Islands, Vesuvius (Italy), e.g. during the eruption of AD 79 which destroyed Pompeii; most of the volcanoes of Suna (Indonesia) and Japan
Classification	volcanic igneous rock, usually of acid composition, but can be intermediate or mafic		

Diorite

Diorite is a coarse-grained plutonic igneous rock, composed of 50 to 75 per cent plagioclase feldspar, and dark-coloured minerals. They are mottled dark grey and white rocks, the mafic minerals tending to look darker than in gabbros. With increasing quartz content, it first becomes *quartz diorite* and then *tonalite*. If alkali feldspar forms more than 10 per cent of the feldspar, it is known as *monzodiorite*. Diorite is distinguished from gabbro on the composition of the plagioclase feldspar (An less than 50 per cent), and also on colour index. Most gabbros have a colour index greater than 40, while anorthosites have a colour index of less than 10. Polished slabs of diorite are used as building stones. The name is derived from the Greek words meaning 'to distinguish'.

Diorite

Diorite

Diorite

	DIORITE
Colour	mottled dark grey and white
Colour index	25–50
Mineralogy	sodic plagioclase, commonly hornblende and often with biotite or augite; may also contain minor amounts of quartz and alkali feldspar (less than 10 per cent each)
Texture	medium- to coarse-grained; where medium-grained, known as *microdiorite*, most of which are porphyritic, although some are equigranular
Structure	often contains fine-grained basic inclusions; occasionally shows orbicular structure
Classification	intermediate plutonic igneous rock QAPF field 10 (and 5 – tonalite, 9 – monzodiorite)
Occurrence	occurs in association with gabbro, tonalite, granodiorite and granite as part of the great granitic intrusions known as batholiths within continental crust
Examples	Nuneaton (England), Esbo (Finland), Laugendal (Norway), Ortles Alps (Italy), Orno (Sweden), Central Peruvian batholith (Peru), Southern California batholith (USA)

Andesite

Andesite, named after the South American Andes, is the intermediate volcanic equivalent of diorite. It is a fine-grained or partly glassy rock, differing from basalt in its lower colour index. Andesites and dacites are the most characteristic, if not the most abundant volcanic rocks in mountain-building regions, forming chains of volcanic islands or ranges close to continental margins. They also occur in continental interiors. The viscous lavas erupt, often quite violently, from chains of composite volcanoes and are associated with deep earthquakes. Lava flows are steep-sided, often showing platy jointing and a blocky structure.

pyroxene phenocryst

plagioclase phenocryst

Porphyritic andesite

Augite andesite

brown surface weathering

Andesite

	ANDESITE		
Colour	blackish brown or greenish	**Examples**	continental settings common on islands and continental margins of the circum-Pacific region, an 'Andesite Line' separating the lines of volcanoes from the interior of the ocean which is free of volcanism; Indonesia and the Lesser Antilles; Colorado Plateau (USA), Mexico, Central America (continental setting); in Europe, found along the northern margins of the Alps, especially the Carpathian Mountains and N Turkey
Colour index	less than 35		
Mineralogy	plagioclase (often zoned from labradorite to oligoclase), pyroxene, hornblende and/or biotite		
Texture	usually porphyritic, phenocrysts commonly plagioclase, augite or hypersthene, occasionally olivine		
Structure	blocky, showing platy jointing		
Classification	intermediate volcanic igneous rock QAPF 9 and 10		
Occurrence	in orogenic (mountain-building) environments i.e. in island arcs and active continental margins; also in		

Syenite

Syenite is an intermediate intrusive igneous rock in which the dominant mineral is alkali feldspar. It was named after Syene, the old Greek name for Aswan, in southern Egypt, although the rock in this area is actually a hornblende granite. A closely related type of rock, known as *alkali feldspar syenite*, is especially striking. It is called *larvikite* after a type found in Larvik, Norway. It contains iridescent alkali feldspars. Known as 'pale Labrador', it is highly decorative and polished slabs are used as building stone. Larvika has been found in the boulder clays of East Anglia, England and is thought to have been transported there by an ice sheet during the Pleistocene. Another related rock is nepheline syenite. This, like syenite, is uncommon.

nepheline

Nepheline syenite

Syenite

sodalite

Sodalite syenite

	SYENITE	
Colour	red, pink, grey or white	
Colour index	10–35	
Mineralogy	alkali feldspar dominant, with subordinate sodic plagioclase, biotite, pyroxene, amphibole and sometimes iron olivine (fayalite); may also contain minor quartz or nepheline	
Texture	coarse to medium-grained; commonly subhedral granular, but tabular feldspar crystals may have a subparallel orientation; occasionally porphyritic	
Structure	drusy structure may be present	
Classification	intermediate plutonic igneous rock QAPF field 7	(and 6 – alkali feldspar syenite)
Occurrence		as stocks, dykes or sills, or around granodiorite plutons; alkali syenites (and their extrusive equivalent trachyte) are the most abundant rock type in many continental alkaline provinces; associated rocks include alkali granite or nepheline syenite, also alkali gabbro; the most important setting is that of crustal extension
Examples		Plauen'scher Grund, near Dresden (Germany); African rift systems; Christina Lake, Rossland district, British Columbia (Canada); Deboullie stock, Maine (USA)

Trachyte

Trachytes are the volcanic equivalent of syenites. Their name comes from the Greek word *trachys*, meaning 'rough', an allusion to their surface roughness. They give rise to the fluidal texture called *trachytic*. Trachytes occur not only as lavas, but also as pyroclastic rocks. These include tuff, pumice flows and ignimbrites with a streaky or blotched appearance due to the alternation of lenses and bands of different colours, composition or texture. Trachyte is used for paving and flooring, because rubbing does not make it shiny. It is also used as a facing stone on buildings.

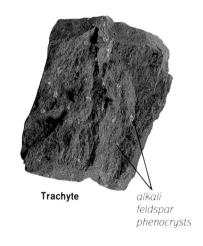

Trachyte   *alkali feldspar phenocrysts*

Trachyte   *feldspar phenocryst*

feldspar phenocryst

Trachyte

		Classification	intermediate volcanic QAPF field 7 (and 6 – alkali trachyte)
	TRACHYTE		
Colour	usually grey, may be white, pink or yellowish		
Mineralogy	essential alkali feldspar; may contain quartz (quartz trachyte) or feldspathoid (feldspathoid-bearing trachyte); if containing alkali pyroxene or amphibole, it is called alkali trachyte	**Occurrence**	a comparatively rare but persistent member of oceanic basaltic suites, may be extruded with rhyolite from the same volcano; occurs as lava flows and very commonly as volcanic domes or plugs
Texture	fine-grained, usually with phenocrysts of one or two feldspars; tabular feldspars in the matrix may show parallel orientation due to flow (trachytic texture); groundmass glass may occur	**Examples**	Drachenfels, Siebengebirge (Germany), Puy de Dôme, Auvergne (central France), Tahiti (Pacific Islands), St. Helena and Ascension (S Atlantic)
Structure	may be vesicular or agglomeratic		

Gabbro

Gabbros are basic intrusive igneous rocks, subdivided according to the relative abundances of orthopyroxene, clinopyroxene, olivine and hornblende. Varieties include *norite* (plagioclase and orthopyroxene), *troctolite* or *troutstone*, so-called because of its spotted appearance (plagioclase and olivine), and *hornblende gabbro* (plagioclase and hornblende with a little pyroxene). Gabbro differs from diorite on the composition of the plagioclase feldspar (An greater than 50 per cent). It is an important member of the ophiolite suite, or rocks representing ancient ocean floor. In this setting, it is affected by low-grade metamorphism. Gabbros are occasionally used as facing stones on buildings, especially the attractive dark varieties, but it is too fragile to make a good construction material.

Troctolite

olivine *plagioclase*

Olivine gabbro *lath-shaped plagioclase*

Layered gabbro

	GABBRO		
Colour	grey to black, speckled with white; troctolite may have black, brown or reddish spots	**Structure**	aligned parallel to layering commonly layered, may show alternating light (feldspar-rich) and dark (pyroxene and/or olivine-rich) layers; may show pegmatitic segregations
Colour index	35–65		
Mineralogy	essential calcic plagioclase, pyroxene and iron oxides; may contain olivine (olivine gabbro) or quartz (quartz gabbro); varieties may contain orthopyroxene and/or hornblende	**Classification**	basic plutonic igneous rock QAPF field 10
		Occurrence	typical of layered intrusions, especially ophiolites, but also in thick sills and other small intrusions
Texture	coarse-grained; often subhedral granular, may show poikilitic or subophitic texture in which plates of pyroxene partly enclose plagioclase crystals; lath-like crystals of feldspar may be	**Examples**	Stillwater, Montana (USA), Muskox (Canada) and Bushveld (South Africa); troctolite on Rhum (Scotland) and the Harz Mountains (Germany); norite common in S Norway

Dolerite

Dolerite is a basic intrusive igneous rock, intermediate in grain size between basalt and gabbro. In North America and Europe, it is often called *diabase*, though many people restrict this term for dolerite which has been altered. In industry, dolerite is called *whin, whinstone, trap* or *traprock*. Dolerites occur as hypabyssal bodies – that is, they are intrusions of smaller grain size and dimensions than plutons, and they form dykes and sills. They are important members of the ophiolite suite, representing ancient oceanic crust. Such 'dyke swarms' represent the repeated intrusion of magma at mid-ocean ridges. In this setting, they are weakly metamorphosed. It is used locally as a building stone. The smaller grain size gives a less fragile rock than gabbro. Dolerites are usually quite uniform bodies but can diversify more than basalts. Such diversification can be caused by the settling of more dense crystals, such as olivine. This is seen more often in sills than in dykes.

Dolerite

Dolerite

	DOLERITE
Colour	black, dark grey or green when fresh; may be mottled black and white
Mineralogy	essential plagioclase, pyroxene and opaque minerals; may contain olivine (olivine dolerite) or quartz (quartz dolerite)
Texture	medium grain size; ophitic texture common; quickly cooled varieties show porphyritic texture with phenocrysts of plagioclase, pyroxene, and sometimes olivine; may contain glass in the groundmass
Structure	may show layering, patches or veins of dolerite pegmatite, also small amounts of glass; vesicles and amygdales may occur
Classification	basic intrusive igneous rock QAPF field 10
Occurrence	as dykes or sills, sometimes forming swarms which may comprise hundreds or thousands of individual bodies, which may radiate out from a single volcanic centre
Examples	very widespread; forms a great belt of Mesozoic intrusions extending from Tasmania and adjacent parts of S Australia across Antarctica and into South Africa

Basalt

Basalts are basic volcanic igneous rocks. They are extremely abundant not only on Earth, where they have erupted throughout known geologic history, but also on the Moon where they formed before the Moon became quiescent 2.5 to 3 billion years ago. Basalts are fine-grained, dark-coloured rocks, essentially composed of plagioclase feldspar and pyroxene. The many types vary according to their chemistry and mineralogy. They include *alkali basalt*, *mid-ocean ridge basalt* (MORB), *olivine basalt* and *tholeiite*. Basalt is distinguished from andesite by its higher colour index (greater than 35). Basalt may show columnar jointing, forming hexagonal pillars of rock. A particularly good example is the 'Giant's Causeway' in Northern Ireland.

Ropy lava

Vesicular basalt

vesicles

amygdales

Amygdaloidal basalt

Basalt

	BASALT		
Colour	black when fresh, may be altered to form a greenish or reddish crust		clinkery (*aa*) or have a ropy appearance (*pahoehoe*); submarine lava flows show pillow structure
Colour index	greater than 35	**Classification**	basic volcanic igneous rock QAPF fields 9 and 10
Mineralogy	essential calcic plagioclase and pyroxene; olivine and minor feldspathoids or quartz may be present	**Occurrence**	forms lava flows either in shallow shield volcanoes or as sheets forming huge lava plateaux; forms the bulk of the ocean floor as well as oceanic volcanoes, islands and floor rift valleys; also dykes and sills
Texture	fine grain-size, may have phenocrysts of olivine, pyroxene or plagioclase		
Structure	commonly vesicular or amygdaloidal, filled with zeolites, carbonate or silica; may contain olivine- or pyroxene-bearing xenoliths; may form columnar joints on cooling; surface forms of lava flows may be rough and	**Examples**	Columbia River, Oregon and Washington (USA), N Australia, Karroo (southern Africa); Baikal Rift (USSR), East African Rift, the Rhine graben, (NW Europe) Hawaii

Anorthosite

Anorthosites are medium- to coarse-grained igneous rocks, composed of at least 90 per cent plagioclase feldspar. The *layered type*, composed of bytownite plagioclase feldspar An_{70-90}), occurs in large layered complexes of any age from Precambrian to late Tertiary. The *massif type*, composed of andesine or labradorite (An_{30-70}), occurs only in Precambrian gneissose rocks between 1,000 and 1,700 years old. A third type occurs in gneissose bands in high-grade metamorphic rocks. Anorthosites, more than 4 billion years old, are important on the Moon. Anorthosites composed of labradorite show an iridescent display of colours.

Anorthosite

labradorite

Anorthosite

Anorthosite

Anorthosite

ANORTHOSITE		troctolites and norites, or as 'massif type anorthosites' in the form of large independent intrusions, characteristically in Precambrian gneiss terrains in layered intrusions at Skaergaard (Greenland), Stillwater, Montana (USA), Bushveld (South Africa) and Muskox (Canada); massif type anorthosites in the Laurentian Mountains, Quebec (Canada), Scandinavia, and Adirondacks, New York (USA)
Colour	white or light grey	
Colour index	0–10	
Mineralogy	essential plagioclase, often with small amounts of pyroxene	
Texture	medium or coarse-grained; feldspar crystals usually over 1 cm (0.4 in) in size, but may range up to 1 m (3.3 ft) and often aligned; pyroxene crystals are sparse, but may be very large	
Structure	may be banded in grain size and texture	
Classification	plutonic igneous rock QAPF field 10	
Occurrence	either as layers in large, mafic intrusions where they are associated with gabbros,	

The row labelled **Examples** corresponds to the right-hand column:

Examples — in layered intrusions at Skaergaard (Greenland), Stillwater, Montana (USA), Bushveld (South Africa) and Muskox (Canada); massif type anorthosites in the Laurentian Mountains, Quebec (Canada), Scandinavia, and Adirondacks, New York (USA)

Pyroxenite

Pyroxenites are ultramafic plutonic rocks. They consist of essential pyroxene, together with up to 40 per cent olivine. They include *clinopyroxenites* (made up almost entirely of clinopyroxene), *orthopyroxenites* (made up almost entirely of orthopyroxene) and *websterites* (containing equal proportions of each). As the amount of olivine increases, they grade into peridotites. Although ultramafic because dark constituents make up more than 90 per cent, pyroxenites are chemically basic because they contain more than 44 per cent silica. There are no true volcanic equivalents of pyroxenites.

Clinopyroxenite

Orthopyroxenite

Pyroxenite

	PYROXENITE
Colour	green, dark green, dark brown or black
Colour index	greater than 90
Mineralogy	essential pyroxene, up to 40 per cent olivine; websterite contains equal amounts of ortho- and clinopyroxene; may also contain hornblende, micas, garnet, feldspar, spinel, ilmenite and sulphides
Texture	medium- to coarse-grained, granular
Structure	may occur as layers, with oriented crystals
Classification	ultramafic, basic plutonic igneous rock
Occurrence	as small independent intrusions (stocks or dykes); present as nodules in basalts, nephelinites and kimberlites; as individual layers in layered gabbros, and in the ultramafic portions of ophiolite complexes
Examples	websterite in Webster County, North Carolina (USA), Troodos Ophiolite Complex (Cyprus), Stillwater Complex, Montana (USA), Bushveld (South Africa), Great Dyke (Zimbabwe), Tulameen district, British Columbia (Canada), Monte Somma, Vesuvius (Italy)

Peridotite

Peridotite is a term used for all ultramafic plutonic igneous rocks that consist essentially of olivine with pyroxene and/or amphibole. The four main types, depending on the relative proportions of the constituent minerals, are *dunite* (more than 90 per cent olivine – see dunite), *harzburgite*, *lherzolite* and *wehrlite*. All contain more than 40 per cent olivine. Peridotites are found in large amounts at the base of ophiolite complexes. Smaller amounts may occur as inclusions in other rocks, representing parts of the mantle. They may also contain biotite and small amounts of garnet and/or spinel. Peridotite has been recovered from the Moon, as blocks in breccias which are thought to represent material from the gabbro-anorthosite Lunar Highlands.

pyroxene cleavage surface

Peridotite

Plagioclase-bearing wehrlite

plagioclase

Wehrlite

	PERIDOTITE		
Colour	dull green to black (see also dunite)	**Alteration**	may alter to serpentine minerals
Colour index	greater than 90	**Occurrence**	the major component of the Earth's mantle, and a minor but important component of the Earth's crust; at the Earth's surface, it occurs as mantle-derived inclusions in basalts, nephelinites or kimberlites, and in the lower part of ophiolite complexes
Mineralogy	essential olivine and orthopyroxene (harzburgite); olivine with minor ortho- and clinopyroxene (lherzolite); essential olivine and clinopyroxene (wehrlite); common accessory minerals are hornblende, mica, spinel, garnet, feldspar		
Texture	granular; also poikilitic, with large crystals of one type enclosing smaller crystals of another	**Examples**	harzburgite in Harzburg, Harz Mountains (Germany); lherzolite at Lhers, Ariège and Pyrenees (France)
Structure	layering may be present		
Classification	ultramafic plutonic igneous rock		

Dunite

Dunite, a variety of peridotite, contains more than 90 per cent olivine. It occurs within linear or *en echelon* bodies known as ultramafic belts, often in association with gabbros, dolerite dykes in parallel sheets, pillow lavas of basalt, and greywackes. This type of complex is known as an *ophiolite suite*, and probably represents an ancient oceanic floor. Dunite also occurs in the cores of stock-like intrusions, which are surrounded by peridotite, pyroxenite, hornblende-magnetite pyroxenite, and an outermost zone of basic rocks. Olivine crystals are thought to accumulate to form dunite because they are formed in the early stages of cooling and have a high density.

Dunite nodule

Dunite

brown weathered surface

Dunite

	DUNITE	
Colour	light to dark green, or shades of yellow and brown	
Colour index	more than 90	
Mineralogy	essential olivine (more than 90 per cent); may contain accessory orthopyroxene, clinopyroxene or chromite	
Texture	medium- to coarse-grained; granular, often sugary texture	
Structure	forms xenoliths, lenses and masses	
Classification	ultramafic plutonic igneous rock	
Alteration	usually altered, partly or completely, to serpentinite	
Occurrence	as nodules in basalts; at the base of layered intrusions; associated with other ultramafic rocks at the base of ophiolite complexes; forming the core of concentrically zoned stocks	
Examples	Dun Mountain, Nelson (New Zealand); in zoned stocks in SE Alaska; in ophiolite complexes, such as Troodos (Cyprus); often associated with harzburgite, a type of periodotite; Gorgona Island (Columbia); at the base of layered intrusions in Stillwater, Montana (USA) and Bushveld (South Africa)	

Carbonatite

Carbonatites, igneous rocks containing more than 50 per cent carbonates, are either plutonic (intrusive) or volcanic (extrusive) in origin. The varieties depend on the nature of the carbonate present, namely calcite, dolomite or other, more unusual carbonates of sodium, calcium and potassium. Carbonatite tuffs have provided excellent environments for the rapid fossilization of land animals. They include well-preserved footprints at Laetoli, Tanzania. A number of mineral deposits, including apatite, copper, fluorite, magnetite, pyrochlore and vermiculite, occur in carbonatites. They are also the world's largest source of rare earth elements.

Carbonatite

Rare earth carbonatite

Carbonatite

Rare earth carbonatite

	CARBONATITE
Colour	light, greyish or yellowish
Mineralogy	largely composed of carbonate minerals, principally calcite and dolomite; may also contain accessory minerals of many different types
Texture	grain-size can be fine, medium or coarse
Structure	intrusives form plugs, dykes and cone-sheets; volcanics form unstable lavas and pyroclastic deposits
Classification	volcanic or plutonic igneous rock
Alteration	superficially cavernous through solution
Occurrence	found as subvolcanic intrusions and as lavas and tuffs, mostly in the stable interiors of continents; most form carbonatite complexes with alkaline and/or ultrabasic volcanic rocks and country rocks affected by intense potassium and/or sodium metasomatism
Examples	Fen Complex, Telemark (Norway), Alno (Sweden), Iron Hill, Colorado and Magnet Cove, Arkansas (USA), Chilwa Province (Malawi); a rock bearing sodium, potassium and calcium carbonates is found at Ol Doinyo Lengai volcano (Tanzania); rare earth carbonatite at Mountain Pass, California (USA)

Phonolite

Phonolite, a fine-grained intermediate igneous rock, was once called *clinkstone*, because of the ringing sound it is supposed to make when hit with a hammer. It is the extrusive equivalent of feldspathoidal syenite. It does not contain enough silica to crystallize quartz and forms some feldspathoidal minerals rather than all feldspar – feldspathoid plus silica equates to feldspar. The most usual feldspathoid is nepheline. Others, including leucite, nosean, hauyne, sodalite or analcime, may also be present. Phonolites occur not only as fine-grained lavas, but also as glassy rocks, pyroclastic rocks, pumice deposits and ash-flow deposits. As with other alkaline rocks they occur in continental rifts, the most important deposits occuring in the Kenya Rift Valley in Africa.

Nosean phonolite *nosean phenocrysts*

Nepheline phonolite

Phonolite

	PHONOLITE	
Colour	dark green to grey, with a greasy lustre	volcanic igneous rock QAPF field 11
Colour index	0–30	
Mineralogy	essential alkali feldspar and feldspathoids; may contain pyroxenes and amphiboles, usually sodic varieties	**Occurrence** forms lava flows, sills and dykes; characteristically in continental rift settings, may be associated with basic and acid extrusive rocks, sometimes carbonatite; also a minor component of oceanic olivine basalt-trachyte associations
Texture	fine-grained, with or without phenocrysts of feldspar, nepheline or, less commonly, leucite; rarely partly glassy; may show trachytic texture (see trachyte)	
Structure	may be fissile (splits into flat sheets); can be vesicular, or show small scale drusy structure, sometimes lined with late stage minerals	**Examples** Kenya Rift Valley (East Africa), Gardar Rift Province (S Greenland) and Tenerife (Canary Islands); leucite phonolite in the Roman Province of central Italy
Classification	alkaline intermediate	

Lamprophyre

Lamprophyre is the name for a distinctive group of igneous rocks characterized by dark minerals with a marked porphyritic texture. They form dykes or small intrusions, and commonly show hydrothermal alteration. The name comes from the Greek word *lampros*, meaning 'glistening'. These rocks are not simply variations of common igneous rock, but they have an unusual mineralogy and chemistry, with higher concentrations of water, carbon dioxide, sulphur, phosphorus, strontium, barium and certain trace elements than other rocks of similar composition. Lamprophyres have restricted occurrence and are usually associated with granites, diorites and syenites.

Lamprophyre

Lamprophyre

Lamprophyre

LAMPROPHYRE

Colour	dark, lustrous rocks
Colour index	35 – 90
Mineralogy	essential biotite and/or amphibole, also clinopyroxene and olivine; feldspars and/or feldspathoids, when present, are restricted to the groundmass; may contain calcite and zeolites
Texture	generally even-grained, with well-shaped crystals; may be porphyritic, with mafic (dark-coloured) minerals occurring as phenocrysts and in the groundmass
Structure	may contain xenocrysts, or xenoliths of mantle of deep crustal origin; ocellar structure common, ocelli being small rounded bodies
Classification	igneous rock, lamprophyre
Alteration	hydrothermal alteration of olivine, pyroxene, biotite and plagioclase (if present) is common
Occurrence	normally as narrow dykes, sills, sheets and plugs, more rarely as lavas; usually associated with diorites and syenites
Examples	Alvik (Sweden); Malchen (Germany), Tjose (Norway), Turij Mis, Kola (USSR), Arizona, California (USA), Cornwall and the Lake District (England), Skaergaard Peninsula (Greenland)

Kimberlite

Geologists now regard kimberlite, the primary source of diamonds, as a variety of lamprophyre. It was named after South Africa's Kimberley diamond mine. The term *blue ground* is used for the unoxidized, slate-blue or blue-green kimberlite that occurs below the superficial oxidized zone. Kimberlite is rare, but is of great interest because of its unusual mineralogy and because it contains rocks brought up from the Earth's mantle. They may form either when melt consolidates at depth, or they may reach the surface as fluidized fragmental kimberlite that forces its way up through a pipe-like structure, called a diatreme. Kimberlite is an important source for gem-quality pyrope crystals called *Cape ruby*.

Kimberlite

 mica

 garnet

Kimberlite

fragments of crystal and rock

Serpentinized kimberlite

	KIMBERLITE		
Colour	bluish, greenish or black	**Classification**	e.g. flow textures ultramafic igneous rock, a variety of lamprophyre; ultrabasic
Mineralogy	olivine (serpentinized), with variable amounts of phlogopite mica, pyroxenes, carbonate and chromite, also minor amounts of e.g. garnet and rutile	**Occurrence**	forms sills, dykes and small diatremes (cylindrical or irregularly shaped bodies drilled through enclosing rocks by gas-charged magma); injected into ancient, upwarped shield areas along broad zones of weakness, also on margins of major structural blocks
Texture	variable grain size characteristic, with fairly large rock or mineral fragments in a fine-grained matrix		
Structure	variable, can be a fragmental tuffaceous or agglomeratic rock, or fragmented material cemented by massive kimberlite, or as a massive rock with igneous textures	**Examples**	Kimberley (South Africa), Tanzania and Navajo-Hopi (S and W USA); Diamantina (Brazil), Sierra Leone, Ghana and Liberia

Ignimbrite

Ignimbrite is an ash-flow tuff (see Ash and Tuff). The name comes from the Latin words meaning 'fire shower'. It consists of fragments of crystal and rock in a matrix of glass shards which are usually welded together. Ignimbrites are formed from pyroclastic flows, which geologists believe were caused by the collapse of a volcanic column of rhyolite or dacite. The flows are highly mobile and may travel 10–100 km (6–62 miles) from the volcanic vent. The particles are extremely hot and, when they come to rest, they weld together. Ignimbrites can cover up to 1000 km² (390 sq mi) in area. No large ignimbrite eruption has ever been observed. Ignimbrite is used as a building store.

Ignimbrite   *pumice fragment*

Ignimbrite

flattened pumice fragments

Ignimbrite

IGNIMBRITE	
Composition	glass of rhyolite or dacite composition; crystals of plagioclase, sanidine (alkali feldspar) or quartz, also of pyroxene, hornblende or biotite; some rock fragments, also pumice
Structure	pumice fragments may be flattened, particularly near the base of the flow, and these are known as fiamme; may show layering or columnar jointing; individual units often very uniform over wide areas but individual units are unstratified and unsorted
Classification	pyroclastic igneous rock, of acid to intermediate composition
Alteration	may devitrify, glass shards being replaced by an intergrowth of feldspar and cristobalite (silica); more extensive devitrification may result in the development of spherulites
Occurrence	often erupt from arcuate fissures around the crest of broad, up-arched domes or caldera faults; also from linear fractures
Examples	Valles Caldera, New Mexico, Valley of Ten Thousand Smokes, Katmai, Alaska and Helena, Montana (USA), New South Wales (Australia), Chile

Agglomerate

Agglomerates are pyroclastic rocks formed from fragments generated directly by volcanic action. These fragments may be individual crystals, or fragments of crystal, glass or rock. Agglomerates are composed of consolidated or unconsolidated coarse material in which rounded grains predominate. The composition of the fragments may range from acid to basic, according to the parent magma (lava). It may also include fragments torn from the side of the volcano. An agglomerate flow occurs when incandescent solid fragments, suspended in hot, expanding gases, rush down the slopes of the volcano, reaching speeds of more than 100 km/h (62 mph).

Volcanic bomb

Spindle-shaped volcanic bomb

Agglomerate

clast of basic volcanic rock

Agglomerate

	AGGLOMERATE		
Composition	individual crystals or fragments of crystal, glass or rock of variable composition	**Classification**	pyroclastic igneous rock
Texture	coarse-grained – greater than 64 mm (2.5 in) – predominantly rounded fragments in a finer-grained matrix; may be highly vesicular	**Occurrence**	formed during explosive volcanic activity, accumulating within the crater, or on the flanks; associated with tuffs and lavas
Structure	may include rounded, ellipsoidal or spindle-shaped volcanic bombs, representing fragments of molten lava ejected from the volcano and gaining their shape on cooling in flight; bombs may have vesicular interiors, and glassy surfaces which have cracked due to	**Examples**	Paricutín (Mexico), Vulcano and Stromboli, Lipari Islands, Etna and Vesuvius (Italy), Mont Pelée (Martinique)

(top right of table) sudden release of gases

Ash and Tuff

Volcanic ash is a pyroclastic rock, composed of fine grains less than 2 mm (0.01 in) in diameter. The ash exploded out of a volcano may fall through the air and settle in beds, called *ash-falls* when unconsolidated, or *ash-fall tuffs* when consolidated. The ash can vary in composition. It may be named *crystal tuff*, *vitric* (glassy) *tuff* or *lithic tuff* (mostly rock fragments). Rock fragments between 2 and 64 mm (0.01–2.5 in) in diameter formed from the ejection of molten lava are called *lapilli*. Ash-flows occur when ash mixed with hot gases is exploded out of volcanoes and flows rapidly downhill. When this material is consolidated, it is called an *ash-flow tuff*. Welded tuffs are called *welded ash-flow tuffs* or *ignimbrites*.

Lithic tuff

Crystal tuff

Tuff

	ASH AND TUFF		
Colour	white or grey powder when newly fallen, either alone or with small vesicular fragments or other pyroclastic matter		rounded or ellipsoidal; loosely textured and porous
		Structure	ash-fall tuffs often well-bedded; ash-flow tuffs unsorted and unstratified
Composition	ash-fall tuffs composed of a mixture of rock fragments, crystals and glass shards; ash-flow tuffs usually glassy, of rhyolite to dacite composition, and may contain crystals of felsic minerals; rock fragments and pumice common	**Classification**	pyroclastic igneous rock
		Alteration	highly susceptible to change; rapidly weathered or otherwise altered, leading to colour differences between successive beds
		Occurrence	associated with explosive volcanic activity; occurs with agglomerates and lava flows; particle size decreases away from the vent because lighter ash carried farthest by the wind
Texture	fine-grained – less than 2 mm (0.01 in) diameter; glass shards show characteristic cusp-shaped outlines; lapilli are usually	**Examples**	nearly all the world's largest and well-known volcanoes

Greisen

Greisen, a coarse-grained, grey, metamorphic rock of glittering appearance, is composed mainly of quartz, pale silvery-green mica, and topaz. It is formed by a process called *greisening* (the pneumatolytic alteration of granite). This process occurs when vapours carrying boron, fluorine and lithium pass through and out of the cooling rock. The original biotite and feldspar of the parent granite are replaced by quartz, lithium-bearing mica (lepidolite or zinnwaldite), tourmaline and kaolinite. Greisen is sometimes of economic importance as a source of tin and tungsten.

Greisen with cassiterite

Greisen

Greisen with beryl

beryl

	GREISEN	Classification	contact metasomatic rock
Colour	greyish, of glittering appearance	**Occurrence**	a pneumatolitically altered granite, forms veins up to a few tens of cm wide which pass gradually into the surrounding granite
Mineralogy	quartz, white mica; may contain topaz, tourmaline, kaolinite, apatite, fluorite; also ore minerals, e.g. cassiterite, rutile, wolframite, chalcopyrite	**Examples**	SW England, Mourne Mountains (Ireland), Klondike district and Esmeralda County, Nevada (USA); younger granites (N Nigeria)
Composition	parent rock granite		
Texture	coarse grain-size; granular		
Structure	as veins, which frequently have a fissure at their centre, filled or partly filled with quartz and ore minerals; the veins may form a well-defined pattern, or may form a closely interconnecting framework which may take over the whole granite		

Skarn

Geologists generally use the term skarn for contact-metamorphosed limestones (calcareous hornfels) that contain other minerals. Skarns are formed when a magma is intruded into limestone, and silicon-. iron- and magnesium-rich fluids react with the calcareous rock to give silicate minerals. Skarns may be associated with ore deposits of sulphides of copper, iron, lead and zinc. They often provide good mineral specimens. The term skarn originally referred to waste rock (gangue) from iron ores. Other rocks called skarn include regionally metamorphosed limestones. These types are not described here.

andradite garnet

Skarn

grossular garnet **Skarn**

Andradite pyrite skarn

	SKARN	**Classification**	contact metamorphic, metasomatic rock
Colour	brown, black, grey; variable on a small scale	**Occurrence**	in the contact aureoles of a variety of plutons
Mineralogy	calcite associated with other minerals including ugrandite garnets, clinopyroxene, olivine, idocrase, periclase, serpentine and calcic amphibole; often forms the host rock for ore minerals such as magnetite and copper sulphides	**Examples**	Crestmore, California (USA), Scawt Hill (Ireland), Skye (Scotland), Dartmoor (England), Doubtful Sound (New Zealand), Oslo (Norway)
Composition	calcareous impure with iron-rich silicates		
Texture	fine- to coarse-grained, granoblastic		
Structure	associated minerals are often clustered in layers, radiating masses or nodules; massive, banded or bedded		

Spotted slate

As its name implies, spotted slate has the texture and structure of slate, but with a spotted appearance. Spotted slates are altered slates, which are usually found alongside unaltered slates. They occur on the outer parts of contact aureoles. They represent low-grade contact metamorphism, just as slate represents the low-grade regional metamorphism of such rocks as shales. Towards the igneous intrusion, the spots become recognizable as ovoid porphyroblasts of cordierite or prismatic crystals of chiastolite, a variety of andalusite. The grains start to recrystallize and any relict slaty cleavage becomes indistinct. The spotted or porphyroblastic rocks then pass into hornfelses of a higher grade adjacent to the intrusion.

Spotted slate

Spotted slate

Spotted slate

	SPOTTED SLATE
Colour	black, purple, grey-green to grey with darker spots
Mineralogy	often too fine-grained for identification by the naked eye; spots are of andalusite and cordierite
Composition	pelitic
Texture	fine-grained
Structure	pre-existing slaty cleavage may be lost and rock becomes more massive; may preserve relict sedimentary bedding and original sedimentary structures such as channels and ripple marks
Classification	low-grade contact metamorphic rock
Occurrence	on the outer regions of contact aureoles in pelitic rocks; associated with slates unaffected by the contact aureole and hornfelses nearer to the intrusion
Examples	Bar-Andlau, Vosges (France), Orijarvi (Finland), Sierra Nevada, California (USA), Aberfoyle slate, Perthshire (Scotland), the Coniston Flags and Skiddaw Slate, Lake District (England)

Hornfels

Hornfelses are hard, fine- to medium-grained, metamorphic rocks, often of a flinty appearance. These baked rocks, formed in the innermost parts of contact aureoles, contain minerals characteristic of high temperatures and low pressures. Some hornfelses are named after the rocks from which they are derived, such as pelitic-, calcareous-, quartzofeldspathic-, and basic hornfelses. Some are named by porphyroblasts present, such as andalusite-, cordierite- and pyroxene-hornfelses. Andalusite porphyroblasts may contain inclusions. In the variety *chiastolite*, the inclusions form a cross-shape. Small igneous intrusions may produce a narrow band of hornfels called a 'baked contact'. Rapid cooling of the magma produces a 'chilled margin' in contact with the hornfels.

Hornfels

Hornfels

Spotted hornfels

	HORNFELS		
Colour	very varied depending on type of source rock		eradicates such structures as schistosity
Mineralogy	very varied, depending on source rock and temperature of heating; andalusite or sillimanite may be present, never kyanite; calcite in calcareous rocks, not aragonite; cordierite and pyroxene are common	**Structure**	medium- to large-scale structures of country rock are preserved
		Classification	medium- to high-grade, contact metamorphic rock
		Occurrence	hornfelses occur in aureoles near to the igneous intrusion and in xenoliths; they occur near, and grading into, slates and spotted slates; common near granite batholiths
Composition	varied, can be any type of rock		
Texture	approximately equidimensional grains typically less than 1 mm (0.04 in); porphyroblasts or phenocrysts may be present; contact metamorphism drastically reduces or	**Examples**	Comrie (Scotland), Donegal (Ireland), Bushveld Complex (South Africa), Bay of Islands (Newfoundland), Mount Wellington (Tasmania)

Marble

Marble is, strictly, a crystalline carbonate rock formed by the metamorphism of limestone. It is much softer than quartzite and is easily scratched with a knife. Calcite marbles effervesce with dilute hydrochloric acid. A famous source of the white marble used for statues is Carrara, Italy. Ophicalcite is a variegated green and white variety, containing forsterite and/ or diopside. Marble is much used in buildings. The Taj Mahal, in Agra, India, is constructed of white calcite marble. Commercially, the term marble includes other rocks and minerals, including alabaster.

pyroxene porphyroblasts

Marble

Ophicalcite

Marble

	MARBLE		
Colour	may be uniformly white and glistening, light brown or grey; also variegated with green, red or black		
Mineralogy	95 per cent calcite and/or dolomite; silicate minerals, such as wollastonite, diopside or forsterite may form from siliceous limestones; many other minerals may be formed depending on impurities in the limestone		
Composition	calcareous		
Texture	medium- to coarse-grained; pure calcite marbles recrystallize towards a granoblastic texture with increasing grade; may show saccharoidal (sugary) texture		
Structure	often massive, but may preserve sedimentary structures such as bedding; fossils may be preserved at low grades only; sometimes folded		
Classification	regional (greenschist, amphibolite or granulite facies) or contact metamorphism		
Occurrence	in most regional metamorphic terrains, also in contact aureoles		
Examples	Cararra (Italy), Vindhyan Hills (central India); in the contact aureole around the Bheinn an Dubhaich granite, Skye (Scotland)		

Quartzite

Quartzites are formed by the regional or contact metamorphism of quartz arenites, siltstones and flints. They are composed essentially of quartz, and usually have a granoblastic texture, where the recrystallized quartz grains are equidimensional and of roughly equal size. Under high pressure, the quartz grains may flatten, leading to the development of foliation. The rock is then termed a quartz schist. The term quartzite may be extended to include rocks containing mica or feldspar. The name feldspathic quartzite is applied to metamorphosed arkoses, which contain a fair amount of feldspar. Quartzites are widespread in metamorphic regions because of the stability of quartz. Quartzite is similar in appearance to marble, but may be distinguished because it is much harder, and, unlike marble, it does not react with dilute hydrochloric acid. Quartzite is used in the glass and ceramic industries. Builders use it for flooring and facing.

chalcopyrite

Quartzite with chalcopyrite

mica-rich layers

Folded quartzite

QUARTZITE		
Colour	white, grey or reddish	
Mineralogy	mostly quartz, may contain some feldspar or mica	
Composition	siliceous	
Texture	medium-grained, granoblastic	
Structure	generally massive, but may sometimes show sedimentary structures, such as bedding or cross-bedding; may show foliation and folding where microscopic layers of mica alternate with layers of quartz	
Classification	regional or contact metamorphism of sandstone	
Occurrence	in regional metamorphic terrains; derived from mature sorted sediments and conglomerates and found associated with other metasediments, such as marble, phyllite or schist	
Examples	Scottish Highlands, County Galway (Ireland), Deccan (India), Guyana, Venezuela	

Slate

Slate is formed from the low-temperature regional metamorphism of fine-grained shales or mudstones. Its chief characteristic is that it easily splits along roughly parallel surfaces, known as *cleavage planes*. These are caused by the alignment of flat mineral crystals, especially micas, during the deformation and compression episodes which turned the original rock into a slate. As slate is a relatively low-grade rock, the aligned crystals are small and the cleavage planes are closely-spaced. Deformation under higher pressures and temperatures produces rocks which contain larger aligned crystals, such as phyllites and schists. Because of its cleavage planes, slate splits into parallel-sided slabs, a property that makes it an important roofing material. Some slates have more than one cleavage direction. The remnants of original sedimentary features, such as graded bedding, may be visible either parallel or slightly inclined to the cleavage. Distorted fossils are found occasionally in slate.

Slate containing iron pyrites

Slate

fossil trilobite

	SLATE	
Colour	mostly grey to black (graphite); may be purple or red (hematite), or green (chlorite)	
Mineralogy	chlorite, micas, graphite, quartz; pyrite may occur in relatively large crystals, due to the reduction of iron in the presence of organic matter	
Composition	pelitic	
Texture	fine-grained, grains too small to distinguish with the naked eye	
Structure	slatey cleavage; look for pale green, ovoid reduction spots; rarely original sedimentary structures and distorted fossils	
Classification	regional metamorphism of	
	greenschist facies	
Occurrence	widespread in regional metamorphic terrains; may be interlayered with metamorphosed greywackes and volcanic rocks	
Examples	Skiddaw (England), Aar Massif, Alps	

Phyllite

The grey or green rock phyllite is formed from the regional metamorphism of clays or shales. It is intermediate in grain size between slate and schist. Phyllite is distinguished from slate by the sheen on the cleavage surface. It is distinguished from schist, because the constituent grains in phyllite are too small to see with the naked eye. The cleavage is well-developed and phyllite splits easily into slabs. The cleavage is caused by the almost perfect parallel alignment of the grains. In phyllites, unlike slates, the fabric is often undulatory, caused by superimposed folds or cenulations. A similar rock, phyllonite, is produced by the retrograde metamorphism of higher grade rocks such as schists. The name phyllite comes from the Greek *phyllos*, meaning 'leaf'.

Graphitic phyllite

Phyllite *crenulations*

Chlorite phyllite

	PHYLLITE		
Colour	light green grey to dark grey	**Classification**	regional metamorphism of greenschist facies
Mineralogy	muscovite, chlorite and quartz; minor constituents are magnetite or pyrite, feldspar and sometimes biotite	**Occurrence**	in regional metamorphic terrains, forming part of a progressive series slate-phyllite-mica schist with increasing metamorphic grade; may be associated with other metamorphosed sediments of the greenschist facies
Composition	pelitic		
Texture	fine-grained, the individual grains too small to identify with the naked eye; may show porphyroblastic texture, with porphyroblasts of albite or manganese-rich garnet		
Structure	shows a well-developed cleavage, the surfaces showing a lustrous sheen; commonly shows one or more sets of crenulations	**Examples**	very common in Eastern and Central Alps, Loch Leven (Scotland), Sulitjelma (Norway), Cooma, New South Wales (Australia), New England (USA), Rhineland Massif (Germany), Ardennes (Belgium)

(microfolds) and lineations

Mica schist

Mica schist is a medium- to coarse-grained rock formed by the regional metamorphism of pelitic rocks. It is characterized by the parallel arrangement of the constituent minerals. This gives it a marked foliation known as *schistosity*. Many rocks possessing this foliation are called schists, but most are mica-rich and formed from pelitic sediments, such as clays, mudstones and shales. They are named after the prominent minerals within them. With increasing pressure, the minerals within a schist gradually change. This is especially noticeable with the porphyroblasts. In a classic terrain in the Scottish Highlands, these appear in the order biotite, garnet, staurolite, kyanite and sillimanite.

Garnet mica schist

garnet porphyroblasts

kyanite porphyroblast

Kyanite biotite schist

Quartz biotite schist

schistosity

	MICA SCHIST		
Colour	greyish and sparkling, white grains of quartz may be visible; colour of porphyroblasts variable	**Structure**	a wheat-sheaf pattern; garnets may form in layers characterized by well-developed schistosity, which may be folded one or more times, and may also show lineations; original sedimentary structures may be preserved
Mineralogy	muscovite and biotite micas, quartz, feldspar and chlorite; may contain porphyroblasts of andalusite, biotite, garnet, staurolite, kyanite or sillimanite if pelitic, or hornblende or actinolite if marly		
		Classification	regional metamorphism of greenschist or amphibolite facies
Composition	pelitic	**Occurrence**	widespread in metamorphic terrains, may be associated with other metasediments
Texture	medium or coarse-grained, commonly porphyroblastic; porphyroblasts may show a preferred direction e.g. an alignment of hornblende needles or arrangement into	**Examples**	Caledonian mountain belt, e.g. Sulitjelma (Norway) and Scotland, the Alps, New England to Georgia (USA), New Zealand, Japan

Gneiss

Gneiss is a foliated rock formed during regional metamorphism. It consists of alternating dark and light bands. The thickness of the bands varies from about 0.5 mm (0.02 in) for the dark layers and up to 40 cm (16 in) or more for the light layers. Many gneisses are quartzo-feldspathic. These are formed from such rocks as arkosic (feldspar-rich) sediments, acid volcanic rocks or granitic rocks. Varieties are distinguished by characteristic minerals (e.g. staurolite gneiss), texture (e.g. augen gneiss), structure (e.g. pencil gneiss), or the parent rock (e.g. granitic gneiss). Gneisses often represent the highest-grade metamorphic rock in an area. They may be associated with, and grade into schists and migmatites.

Streaky gneiss

Banded gneiss

felsic layer

mafic layer

Augen gneiss

	GNEISS		
Colour	commonly formed of alternating dark and light (white, pink or grey) bands		crystals, particularly well-shown by feldspar
Mineralogy	quartz and feldspar, may also contain biotite and/or hornblende, also various porphyroblasts, such as garnet, staurolite, sillimanite or cordierite	**Structure**	bands and foliations may be folded one or more times; shows other structures, such as waves, streaks and veins
Composition	varied, may be igneous or sedimentary	**Classification**	regional metamorphism of amphibolite or granulite facies
Texture	medium- to coarse-grained, usually coarser than schists; bands and lenses of alternating granular and flaky minerals, less than 50 per cent crystals showing parallel orientation; may show augen (eye-shaped)	**Occurrence**	widely distributed in regional metamorphic terrains, often of Precambrian age
		Examples	Precambrian shield regions of Scandinavia, Canada, Brazil, Australia; pelitic gneisses in the Vosges (France) and the Black Forest (Germany); granitic gneiss in the Alps

Migmatites

Migmatites are complex rocks formed at high temperatures, comprising a dark, schist-like or gneissose component (*paleosome*) and a light-coloured granitic component (*neosome*). Most geologists agree that they represent stages in the formation of granite magmas by partial melting of the existing rock. The variety *agmatite* consists of angular blocks of paleosome surrounded by veins of neosome, resembling breccia. In *nebulite* ('cloudy' migmatite), the components grade into each other, giving a diffuse appearance. The *ptygmatic veins* that occur in some migmatites are small, intensely folded veins of neosome. Migmatites are used as a building stone and occasionally as polished slabs for decorative use.

Migmatite

Migmatite

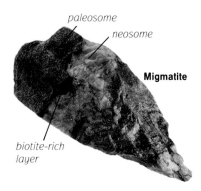

paleosome

neosome

Migmatite

biotite-rich layer

	MIGMATITES	
Colour	a mixture of a dark coloured component (also called host rock) and a white, pink or grey granitic component	
Mineralogy	host rock minerals are the same as for schists and gneisses of high metamorphic grade; essential granitic minerals are quartz and alkali feldspar	
Composition	usually felsic or intermediate	
Texture	medium- to coarse-grained components may have the texture of schists or gneisses, including augen structures	
Classification	high grade metamorphism	
Occurrence	often found in old Archaean rocks in continental shield areas (old stable areas which have not been subjected to major tectonic action) where deep erosion has revealed rocks formed at depth; also in smaller bodies in contact aureoles close to large granite intrusions	
Examples	common in Finland, Canada, Massif Central (France), Scottish Highlands	

Amphibolite

Amphibolites are usually formed by the metamorphism of basic igneous rocks, namely basaltic tuffs, lava, or intrusive dolerite. But some are also derived from marls (calcium-rich pelitic rocks). They are formed under conditions of medium temperature, that is around 600°–750°C (1100°–1380°F). The closely related rock epidote amphibolite contains epidote, albite and hornblende. It forms from the same kinds of rocks, but at slightly lower temperatures. Hornblende granulite is formed at higher temperatures. It contains orthopyroxene as well as hornblende and plagioclase.

Amphibolite

Garnet amphibolite

Schistose amphibolite

schistosity

	AMPHIBOLITE		
Colour	green to dark green or black; often speckled or striped with white or grey		occasionally contain porphyroblasts of garnet
Mineralogy	hornblende (or occasionally actinolite or tremolite) and plagioclase; minor amounts of quartz, garnet, biotite, diopside cummingtonite	**Structure**	often forms disrupted lenses and fragments within schists
		Classification	regional metamorphic rock of amphibolite facies
Composition	mafic or calc-pelitic	**Occurrence**	widely distributed in old shield areas and younger orogenic belts; often associated with garnet-, kyanite-, staurolite- or sillimanite-bearing schists and gneisses
Texture	may be massive, medium-grained, equigranular rocks or foliated *(hornblende schists)* or lineated; may show dark and light bands, the individual stripes being 1 mm – 2 cm (0.04 – 0.8 in) thick; relict igneous textures and structures are sometimes preserved; may		
		Examples	Adirondacks, New York (USA), Broken Hill, NSW (Australia), Grampian Highlands (Scotland), Connemara (Ireland), SW Greenland

Glaucophane schist

Glaucophane schists are rocks with a characteristic blue colour, hence their alternative name, blueschists. They occur in regions where rocks have been deeply buried but at relatively low temperatures. This situation occurs along subduction zones, where cold, mostly mafic ocean crust is pulled down as a slab along destructive plate margins. Associated rocks include eclogites and so-called ophiolitic debris, containing shales and greywackes formed on the ocean floor. Blueschists do not occur in Precambrian rocks. Some geologists have argued that this fact demonstrates that plate tectonic processes did not operate in the Precambrian.

Glaucophane schist

Glaucophane schist

garnet porphyroblast

Glaucophane schist

	GLAUCOPHANE SCHIST		
Colour	dark blue or purple		metamorphism
Mineralogy	abundant glaucophane (a blue amphibole) with quartz, albite, jadeite, garnet or chlorite	**Occurrence**	uncommon; mainly in orogenic mountain building belts such as the Alps/ Himalayas and the circum-Pacific region
Composition	mafic	**Examples**	Channel Islands, Ballantrae
Texture	fine- to medium-grained; poorly schistose with alignment of glaucophane needles		(Scotland), Anglesey (Wales), Coastal Range, California (USA), Svalbard (Norway), Sanbagawa and Sangun (Japan); Western Alps, New Caledonia (Canada)
Structure	shows chaotic relationships in the field, forming broken blocks along with ophiolite fragments in a sheared matrix of shale, greywacke or serpentinite; may contain lenses of eclogite		
Classification	high pressure, low temperature regional		

Eclogite

Eclogite is an attractive rock containing green omphacite and red garnet. It often has a banded structure and may contain large porphyroblasts. Eclogite has the same chemical composition as basalt, but its specific gravity is about 3.5 as compared with 3.0 for basalt. Its higher density reflects its formation at high pressures and at great depths. There are three groups of eclogites. Common eclogites (Group C) are probably metamorphosed dolerite dykes or sills, or basalt lava. Magnesium-rich garnet pyroxenites (Group G) originate in the upper mantle. Some geologists consider them to be igneous rocks. Iron- and sodium-rich ophiolitic eclogites (Group O) were formed when oceanic crust was deeply buried by subduction.

Eclogite

Eclogite

pyroxene

garnet

Eclogite

ECLOGITE

Colour	red and green
Mineralogy	essential minerals are garnet and the aluminium-containing clinopyroxene omphacite; accessory minerals include hornblende, zoisite, quartz, kyanite, mica, rutile, olivine, glaucophane, epidote and dolomite, but never plagioclase
Composition	mafic
Texture	medium- to coarse-grained; often large garnet or pyroxene porphyroblasts
Classification	high pressure, low-, medium- or high-temperature regional metamorphism
Structure	often massive and banded
Occurrence	common eclogites as small bodies in migmatites or gneisses; garnet pyroxenites as nodules and lenses in kimberlites, basic lavas and ultramafic rocks; ophiolitic eclogites as intercalations and lenses in blueschists, often with serpentinites and metamorphosed sediments
Examples	Group C: Fichtelgebirge and Saxony (Germany), Sausalpe (Austria), Highland Region (Scotland), and W Norway; Group G: Bohemian Massif, SW Norway, South Africa and Oahu (Hawaii); Group O: California (USA), Sesia-Lanzo, Piedmont (Italy) and Wallis Alps (Switzerland)

Serpentinite

Serpentinite is a soft, compact metamorphic rock composed of serpentine minerals. It is formed by the hydrous alteration (alteration through the addition of water) of olivines and pyroxenes in ultramafic rocks. Some relict (unaltered) rock may remain. Attractive varieties are used for ornaments and facing stones. The Inuits of North America and the Lapps of northern Europe have used soapstones and serpentinites for artefacts. It is also used as a source of asbestos, chromite (for chromium), refractories, and talc (for paper making).

Serpentinite

Serpentinite with stichtite

stichtite

Garnet serpentinite

	SERPENTINITE	
Colour	pale green to greenish black, often with red or bright green streaks or blotches; weathered surfaces are yellow-orange to red-brown; has a dull waxy appearance	
Mineralogy	wholly or mainly serpentine minerals antigorite, chrysotile or lizardite; may contain minor amounts of olivine, pyroxene and spinel from the parent rock, and also minerals such as talc, chlorite and iron oxides	
Composition	ultramafic	
Texture	medium- to coarse-grained; compact; has a smooth to splintery fracture	
Structure	may be massive, with relics of ultramafic parent rock, or sheared, showing many polished slip surfaces cut by intercrossing veins of fibrous chrysotile (asbestos)	
Classification	low-temperature, low pressure, hydrous alteration product	
Occurrence	stocks, dykes and lenses, often grading into peridotite	
Examples	the Lizard, Cornwall (England), Alps, Stillwater Complex, Montana (USA), Quebec (Canada), Cuba, New Zealand, Norway, Yugoslavia, Himalayas, Cuba, Phillipines, Albania, Cyprus	

Mylonite

Mylonite is a cataclastic rock formed during dynamic metamorphism. The term *cataclasis* comes from the Greek words meaning 'breaking down'. Mylonite is formed where rocks react by ductile flow, whereas *fault breccia* is formed where rocks react by breaking. In mylonite, the grain size gradually decreases as the rock is strained, but it increases as the rock starts to recover. The rock being deformed can be of any kind. As it is ground up, the original fragments form a smaller and smaller proportion of the whole rock. Unlike fault breccia, mylonite is always a cohesive rock.

Mylonite

Mylonite

Mylonite

feldspar porphyroclast

	MYLONITE		
Composition	variable		
Texture	complex; strained porphyroclasts (relict crystals) are set in a finer-grained matrix formed by the crushing of minerals of different physical properties; fragments of original rock (protolith) may form more than 50 per cent of the rock ('protomylonite'), 10–50 per cent ('ultramylonite') or less than 10 per cent (mylonite); porphyroclasts may be lozenge-shaped, forming an augen rock, or may be reduced to a fine-grained aggregate which is streaked out as a 'flaser' structure to		give a layered or banded structure; may eventually recrystallize, leading to a coarsening of grains
		Classification	dynamic metamorphic rock
		Occurrence	forms at depth in zones of shearing, almost invariably occurring in regional metamorphic gneisses or granulites at the margins of orogenic belts; belts of mylonites and other cataclastic rocks are characteristic of Precambrian orogenic belts, are commonly vertical, and often many kilometres wide
		Examples	San Andreas Fault, California (USA), Insubric Line (Central Alps)

Conglomerates

Conglomerates are *rudaceous* (coarse-grained) rocks composed of rounded fragments set in a mass of fine- to medium-sized grains (the *matrix*). The rounded fragments range in size from pebbles to boulders. They may consist of almost any hard rock, especially such weather-resistant types as chert or quartzite. Deposited from fast-moving water, conglomerates form on beaches and river beds. They are often formed during marine transgressions – that is, when the sea floods a large area relatively rapidly. Hence, conglomerates often occur above unconformities. They can mark the bottom of a new sequence of rocks and form a major geological boundary.

Conglomerate

quartzite pebbles

Conglomerate

chert pebbles

Polished puddingstone

Polished conglomerate

CONGLOMERATES	
Colour	variable and dependent on type and proportion of pebbles
Mineralogy	pebbles very varied in composition; variable proportions of sand or silt matrix which may be cemented to a greater or lesser extent by calcite or silica
Texture	coarse-grained mixture of two main components, one fine- to medium-grained, the other rounded fragments of pebble to boulder size
Structure	little internal structure; fossils rare
Occurrence	often found above unconformities and associated with sandstones and arkoses
Examples	puddingstone in Hertfordshire (England) and Lucerne (Switzerland), the Precambrian Ingleton Series of N England, Triassic conglomerates of eastern USA, gold-bearing conglomerates of Witwatersrand (South Africa); modern gravels are ubiquitous in river beds and beaches

Breccias

Breccias, like conglomerates, are coarse-grained rocks. They differ from conglomerates in that the large fragments set in the fine- to medium-grained matrix are angular and unworn. Because large and heavy fragments are much more easily rounded by erosion during transport than smaller grains, the angular fragments must not been moved far from the source rock. The angular fragments in some breccias are formed by landslides or the heaps of scree (talus) at the foot of steep slopes. Others are formed when limestone caves collapse. Fault breccia is produced by the fragmentation of rocks during fault movements.

Breccia

Fault breccia

Breccia

BRECCIAS

Colour variable

Mineralogy rock fragments may be of any rock type; variable proportions of sand or silt matrix, often cemented by calcite or silica

Texture coarse-grained mixture of two components, one of fine- to medium-size grains, the other of angular fragments of pebble to boulder size

Occurrence often occur above unconformities and associated with conglomerate, arkose or sandstone; may occur close to a fault zone

Examples the 310 m (1020 ft) thick Cow Head Breccia of Newfound-land (USA) is especially spectacular; it is found in dolomites and limestones of Beekmantown, Pennsylvania and Siyeh Mountains (USA), Cotham marble, Bristol (England) and Eilean Dubh dolomite, Sutherland (Scotland)

Till and Tillites

Till, also called *boulder clay*, is the unconsolidated matter deposited by glaciers and ice sheets from the Pleistocene glaciation. The consolidated form is called *tillite*. Tillites are older rocks from the four other major glaciations. Till is characterized by a wide range of particle sizes and types of fragments, the largest boulders weighing several tonnes. The material was originally gathered up by moving bodies of ice, transported, and finally dumped when the ice melted. This is an example of erosion where the material is transported with virtually no sorting or grading. Till and tillite are important indicators of glaciation and possibly of a major Ice Age in Earth history.

Tillite

clast

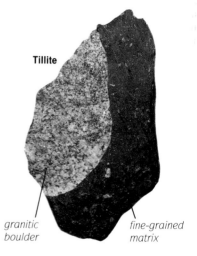

Tillite

granitic boulder

fine-grained matrix

Tillite

rock fragment

	TILL AND TILLITES	
Colour	tills are red-brown to grey and when consolidated to tillites are dark grey to greenish black	in N Germany and Britain (e.g. the Yorkshire coast), and in Canada and the N USA; older tillites include the Dwyka Tillite of South Africa, the Talchir Boulder Bed of India and the Huronian tillites of Canada; modern boulder clays are forming in Greenland, Spitzbergen and Antarctica
Mineralogy	rocks of sedimentary, igneous or metamorphic origin set in a matrix of clay and/or sand-grade material	
Texture	fine to very large grain size; angular to rounded pebbles, cobbles and boulders in finer matrix	
Structure	no bedding or internal structures	
Occurrence	glaciated terrains of any rock type	
Examples	boulder clays formed during the Ice Age in the Pleistocene epoch are found	

Sandstones: Quartz arenites

Quartz arenites. or orthoquartzites, are *arenaceous* (medium-grained) sandstones containing a high proportion of quartz. Some were deposited in water, usually in shallow marine environments, while others, termed *aeolian*, were wind-blown sands deposited in desert environments. Porous sandstones are important as aquifers for ground water and as reservoirs for oil and natural gas. Well-cemented sandstones are used in building. Finer-quality sands are used in glass manufacture. Where little high-quality brick clay is available, as in Germany, silica sand is used in calcium silicate bricks. *Ganister* is a quartz arenite with good refractory properties used to line furnaces.

Desert sandstone

bedding disturbed by burrows **Quartz arenite**

Quartz arenite

Orthoquartzite

bedding

SANDSTONES

Colour	varies greatly; often white or pale grey when derived from shallow water, such as a beach; red when of desert origin; in greensands, the colour is due to precipitation of glauconite
Mineralogy	over 95 per cent quartz grains; varying amounts of matrix and cement affect porosity and strength
Texture	medium-grained; mostly well-sorted and rounded; wind-blown grains are well-rounded with a frosted surface
Structure	bedding in marine sandstones is usually easily seen and sedimentary structures, e.g. cross-stratification and graded bedding, are common, as are a variety of fossils and concretions; in aeolian sandstones, large scale cross-bedding (dune-bedding) is often seen
Occurrence	ubiquitous; found in association with most sedimentary rock types
Examples	quartzites of Holyhead (N Wales), Hartshill and the Stiperstones, Shropshire (England), Eriboll (NW Scotland) and Fontainebleau (France); Lower Cretaceous greensands are common in North America

Sandstones: Lithic arenites

Quartz makes up a much lower proportion of the grains in lithic arenites than in quartz arenites, though it is still the main component. Besides quartz, lithic arenites contain a variety of other mineral fragments, that can be derived from any rock that can give sand-sized particles. However, feldspar grains form a relatively minor component. Lithic arenites, or *litharenites*, are a major rock group. They comprise a high proportion of the sandstones found around the world. They are formed in rivers, deltas, shallow seas and sea basins.

Lithic arenite

Polished slab

Lithic arenite

	SANDSTONES
Colour	variable
Mineralogy	wide variety of rock fragments with up to about 75 per cent quartz grains; less than 15 per cent fine-grained material
Texture	medium-grained; may range widely in degrees of sorting and angularity of grains
Structure	bedding is often apparent as are sedimentary structures; fossils and various concretions may be present
Occurrence	found in association with most other sedimentary rock types relatively close to source of lithic grains
Examples	found among many sandstones of all ages; Old

Red Sandstone-age rock of the Welsh borderland (Britain), Palaeocene rocks of Dakota (USA), Permian rocks of India and Australia, and Tertiary rocks of the northern Mediterranean

Sandstones: Arkoses

Arkoses are feldspar-rich sandstones that are derived from granitic rocks and gneisses. The feldspar is mostly alkali feldspar, usually microcline. Arkoses contain little fine-grained matrix material and the feldspar grains are angular. This often gives the rocks a gritty appearance and feel. Because feldspars weather to clay minerals, arkoses generally form in relatively dry or cold climates. In humid environments, their formation depends on rapid burial and removal from circulating water. The red or pink colour is usually derived from the feldspar, but some hematite may also be present.

Coarse-grained arkose

Arkose

Arkose

	SANDSTONES	
Colour	grey, pink, or red	
Mineralogy	contains more than 25 per cent feldspar and usually up to 50 per cent; the remainder is often quartz with some biotite and muscovite; calcite or iron oxide cement	
Texture	medium-grained, usually at the coarsest end of the range, with up to 15 per cent of a fine-grained matrix; the grains are angular	
Structure	bedding may be well developed or obscure; cross-lamination and cross-bedding is common; fossils are rare	
Occurrence	formed by the degradation of granites and granite gneisses, followed by transport over only short distances and deposition in rivers, lakes or shallow seas; arkoses often occur above unconformities near to granitic rocks and are associated with granite-derived conglomerate	
Examples	Torridon sandstone (Scotland), the Vosges Mountains (France), the Black Forest, (Germany), the sandstones of the Californian Coastal Range (USA), and among the sandstones of the Millstone Grit (N England)	

Sandstones: Greywackes

Greywackes are typically dark, hard rocks formed by turbidity currents. These currents occur when a mass of sediment at the top of a continental slope (the edge of a continental shelf) is set in motion, perhaps by an earthquake. The sediment, forming a dense solid-liquid mixture, slumps rapidly down the slope. It is dumped at the bottom, giving rise to a formation containing greywackes. The nature and speed of turbidity currents was recognized only 20 years after one such underwater avalanche broke 12 submarine cables to the east of Newfoundland in 1929. Greywackes are usually well cemented rocks, as the sediments are rapidly buried and often subjected to mild metamorphism and tectonic processes.

Greywacke

Calcareous greywacke

Greywacke

carbonaceous silt pebbles

	SANDSTONES
Colour	usually dark, from grey to black, sometimes greenish
Mineralogy	grains of quartz, feldspar and rock fragments; the fine-grained matrix cannot be distinguished by the naked eye; chlorite may impart a green colour
Texture	medium-grained; usually poorly sorted, angular grains set in a fine-grained matrix which comprises at least 15 per cent of the rock
Structure	often massive, with graded bedding common; beds are coarse-grained at the bottom and grade through to silt or clay at the top; fossils very rare; commonly have slump structures
Occurrence	formed typically in rapidly subsiding marine basins by turbidity currents, often off continental margins and in association with volcanics
Examples	in the Lower Palaeozoic rocks of Wales, Ireland and the Southern Uplands of Scotland; the Devonian-Carboniferous rocks of SW England and Germany; the Mesozoic rocks of California, Washington and Alaska (USA); and the Tertiary Waitemata Group of N New Zealand

Siltstones

Siltstones are composed of silt grains. They are intermediate in grade between sandstones and shales. The gritty feel when ground between the teeth distinguishes them from shales. Some grains in siltstones may be visible to the naked eye, especially shiny mica, quartz and feldspar crystals. Silt is a well-known deposit in lakes and slow-flowing rivers. It also occurs in large quantities in seas not too close to the shore and, in lesser amounts, in glacial deposits. Bedding is often more clearly visible than in shales, and may bear more relationship to that found in finer-grained sandstones. Ripples can give rise to some cross-stratification. Like other mudrocks, siltstones may contain nodules formed by cementing minerals such as calcite, pyrite and chert. Fossils are often abundant in siltstones.

Red siltstone

Leached siltstone

Green siltstone

	SILTSTONES		
Colour	shades of grey to black and brown to pale brown or yellow		
Mineralogy	coarser grains of quartz, micas and feldspars set in a very fine-grained matrix including clay minerals; some concretions of other minerals may be present		
Texture	fine-grained, with grain sizes between 0.004 and 0.06 mm (0.0002 – 0.002 in); grittiness by feel or by grinding softer specimens between the teeth distinguish siltstones from shales		
Structure	fine bedding is common; also small-scale sedimentary structures, such as ripple marks		
Occurrence	can occur in many sedimentary sequences throughout the world, often found alongside shales and sandstones		
Examples	late Precambrian rock of Islay and the Caithness (Scotland), Devonian portage group in New York and most modern sediments of the Mississippi Delta (USA), the Hasawnah formation and at Wadi Ash Shati (Libya)		

Clays, Shales and Mudstones

The finest grained detrital rocks are soft, plastic clays which occur only in young formations. The particles are invisible to the naked eye and clay feels smooth when worked. Shales are finely laminated or bedded rocks that split into fine layers, whereas mudstones are quite massive and well-consolidated. Clays accumulate in the deepest parts of lakes and seas where the gentlest water movements can transport the smallest particles. Fossils are often abundant. These rocks are often coloured black by carbonaceous material, or red by oxides of iron. Greenish hues are also common. Together with siltstones, these rocks are termed mudrocks.

Shale

Carbonaceous shale

Lime mudstone

bedding

Banded mudstone

bedding

	CLAYS, SHALES AND MUDSTONES
Colour	black through grey to off-white, browns, reds and dark blues/greens
Mineralogy	mainly clay minerals and detrital quartz, feldspar and micas; none can be seen by the naked eye
Texture	very fine grain size – less than 0.004 mm (0.0002 in); very smooth to the touch, shales may be worked between the teeth without a gritty feel
Structure	fine bedding in shales; may show sun-cracks, rain-prints and various marks left by organisms on mud flats
Occurrence	often occur in association with limestones and sandstones as part of repeating cycles, reflecting marine transgressions and regressions with near-shore, shallow and deep water environments
Examples	ubiquitous; also the black shales of the Lower Palaeozoic of England, Wales and Germany; the Precambrian Nonesuch Shale of Michigan (USA) is copper-bearing; the fossil-rich Burgess Shales (Australia)

Loess

Loess consists of fine detrital material that has been transported and deposited by winds. It is also known as Aeolian clay after *Aiolos*, the Greek god of the winds. It differs from muds and clays deposited in water, because it contains few or no clay minerals. Instead, it consists of extremely small, angular fragments of rock-forming minerals, especially quartz. They appear originally to have come from glacial outwash or from deserts. Loess can form high cliffs, often revealing vertical tubes with calcite linings. It is often unstratified and unconsolidated. Deposits in China and Europe can be quite thick but are remarkably uniform throughout. Loess is easily washed out and reworked by the action of water. Thus it is uncommon to find loessic rocks formed before Pleistocene times. However, one recently discovered example is from Late Precambrian rocks in northern Scandinavia. *Adobe*, a similar calcareous deposit, occurs in the Mississippi valley in the USA.

Compact loess

Poorly consolidated loess deposit

	LOESS	
Colour	yellow, brown, buff and grey	
Mineralogy	rock-forming minerals, too small to be seen by the naked eye	
Texture	very fine-grained; earthy and porous; easily crumbles to the touch	
Structure	poor or no bedding apparent; few fossils	
Occurrence	loess is formed from minute wind-blown particles of probable glacial origin; the rocks associated with it are thus very varied and unhelpful for identification purposes	
Examples	large late Pleistocene deposits of great thickness in China, the Mississippi valley	area (USA), central Europe and eastern South America; the 'loessite' of late Precambrian rocks of N Norway is one of the few positively identified pre-Pleistocene loess deposits

Fossiliferous limestones

Fossiliferous limestones consist of a large number of fossils held together mainly by a calcite cement. Biohermal limestones, formed from colonies of algae or coral and the animals living in them, are formed in shallow water, as also are biostromal limestones formed from beds made up of the shells of bottom-living organisms. Pelagic limestones, formed in deep water, consist of the skeletons of floating organisms, usually plankton. Occasionally, fossiliferous limestones form in fresh water. The types may be distinguished by the nature of the fossils they contain.

Shelly limestone

Shelly limestone

Shelly limestone

	FOSSILIFEROUS LIMESTONES	
Colour	variable; white, grey or cream to red, brown or black with increasing impurities	
Mineralogy	finely divided calcite mud containing larger crystals from animal skeletons; also varying amounts of chert, silt or mud	
Texture	variable; from fine-grained compact, porcelain-like to very coarse; texture depends on the number and type of fossils present	
Structure	bedding often apparent; the fossils may be complete or fragmented; in reef limestones the stucture of the reef may be preserved; often cut by veins of calcite	
Other tests	effervesces with dilute hydrochloric acid	
Occurrence	widely distributed, mainly as three types: biohermal, biostromal and pelagic limestones	
Examples	bichermal include some Carboniferous limestones at Durham (England) and the modern Great Barrier Reef (Australia); biostromal types include Purbeck Marble in Dorset (England), Eden and Maysfield beds of SW Ohio (USA), Carinthia (Austria) and modern deposits in Florida; pelagic types include Eocene limestones of the Nile valley (Egypt)	

Oolitic and Pisolitic limestones

Oolitic limestones are carbonate rocks made up mostly of ooliths (or *ooids*). They often resemble fish roe. Ooliths are formed by the precipitation of carbonate in concentric layers around a central nucleus, such as a shell fragment or a quartz grain. Pisoliths are larger grains that appear to have formed under different conditions from ooliths. A related particle, an *oncoid*, superficially resembles an oolith, but it is of algal origin. Ooliths are being formed today in the Gulf, the Red Sea, the shallow waters near the Bahamas, and the Great Salt Lake of Utah in the USA. Pisoliths occur in the coastal plans around the Gulf.

Oolitic limestone

Oolitic limestone

Pisolitic limestone

oncoids

	OOLITIC AND PISOLITIC LIMESTONES		
Colour	white through yellow to browns and reds	**Other tests**	effervesces with dilute hydrochloric acid
Mineralogy	usually calcite ooliths in varying amounts of a finer-grained calcite matrix, but ooliths of dolomite, hematite and silica occur; some detrital quartz or clays may be present	**Structure**	often current bedded; varying amounts of fossil fragments
		Occurrence	in warm, shallow, strongly agitated seas
Texture	spheres or oval shapes having a concentrically zoned inner structure, possibly dispersed, in a fine-grained matrix; ooliths are up to 1 mm (0.04 in) in diameter; pisoliths are between 2 and 10 mm (0.08 – 0.4 in) in diameter	**Examples**	Middle Jurassic Great Oolite (S England); oolitic sands are found around the Red Sea and the Gulf; pisoliths occur in sabkha zones (coastal plains), around the Gulf

Chalks

Chalk, a pure form of limestone, is usually found in thick beds. Most chalks were formed during the Cretaceous period. This period – from 140 to 65 million years ago – was named from *creta*, the Latin word for 'chalk'. This was because high sea levels gave rise to the large areas of shallow sea needed for chalk deposition. Some chalks have layers just a few centimetres thick which have been more thoroughly cemented. Such *hardgrounds* were formed during periods of low depositon. The porous chalks of Western Europe are important as aquifers. But other well-cemented chalks are much denser and, hence, much less porous. The main constituents of chalk are the calcareous remains of micro-organisms called *coccoliths* and *foraminifera*. The pure white chalks contain more than 90 per cent calcium cabonate. Chalks often contain nodules of flint or chert, together with large fossils. A common and well-studied example of a large fossil is the sea urchin *Micraster*.

Chalk

Chalk

fossil starfish

	CHALKS	
Colour	white, grey or yellow	
Mineralogy	mainly calcite, chalk is a very pure limestone containing little silt or mud; silica, present as flint or in marcasite, is common	limestones (made up of the skeletons of floating organisms) formed in shallow, open seas free from most other sediments; most are Cretaceous in origin but some are being formed today
Texture	fine-grained, finely porous, friable (crumbles easily) or compact	
Structure	usually well bedded in thick extensive successions, with little small-scale bedding apparent; fossils usually present; flint and marcasite nodules common	**Examples** the Weald (SE England), Antrim (Northern Ireland), France, Kansas (USA); recent chalks in the Black Sea; modern chalks are forming in Alpine lakes
Other tests	effervesces with and dissolves in dilute hydrochloric acid	
Occurrence	chalks are pelagic	

Dolomites

Dolomites almost invariably began to form as lime deposits. At some stage, or stages, during their subsequent conversion into rock, the calcium carbonate was replaced by dolomite by reaction with magnesium-rich waters. Most limestones contain some magnesium carbonate. Geologists usually use the term dolomite only for rocks with a high proportion of the mineral dolomite. They are more abundant than those with magnesite as their main component. The process of dolomitization occurs either shortly after deposition of the sediment, or some time later when the rock is already well cemented. The process of conversion of calcite to dolomite involves a 12 per cent reduction in volume. This can result in a highly porous rock, which is commonly a reservoir rock for oil and natural gas. Dolomite (also known as magnesian limestone) is a source of magnesium oxide, which is used as an antacid and in insulating materials. Other uses of dolomite are as a refractory material and a building stone. Dolomite was named after the French mineralogist D. Dolomieu.

Dolomite

Dolomite

	DOLOMITES		
Colour	white, cream or grey, weathering to brown or pinkish		to dilute hydrochloric acid, unlike limestones
Mineralogy	a mixture of calcite and dolomite; magnesite may be present at high magnesium concentrations; lesser amounts of other detrital materials and cherts	**Occurrence**	mainly among other limestones and often in association with salt and gypsum deposits
Texture	coarse, medium or fine-grained; often compact but may be porous	**Examples**	NW Scotland (Sailmhor Formation), NE England (magnesian limestone); Saudi Arabia (Jurassic oil reservoir rocks); NE Italy; Bighorn, Wyoming and Niagara (USA)
Structure	often massive with any apparent bedding being on a large scale; concretions often present; fossil remains are usually destroyed by dolomitization; well jointed		
Other tests	shows no obvious reaction		

Travertine and Tufa

Travertine and tufa are composed almost wholly of calcite. They are precipitated from water containing calcium carbonate in solution (as bicarbonate). Some form when water evaporates around springs or in caves. Others are created around geysers and hot springs by a change in temperature and/or the carbon dioxide content. Travertine is a quite compact rock, but tufa (or calc-tufa) is a porous, sponge-like rock. Travertine may be banded in various colours and shades due to staining by iron oxides. The dripstone deposits in caves give rise to the well-known features, stalactites and stalagmites.

Tufa

Travertine marble

Tufa

	TRAVERTINE AND TUFA		
Colour	white, cream or yellow, often stained brown to red		caves and around springs (hot or cold) and geysers
Mineralogy	predominantly calcite, stained to varying degrees by iron oxides	**Examples**	Auvergne (France), Tuscany and near Rome, especially around Tivoli (Italy), Dubois, Wyoming, and the Great Basin region in the western USA
Texture	compact to earthy; crumbles easily		
Structure	travertine may contain bands picked out in different amounts of iron oxide staining; stalactites and stalagmites show many small concentric 'growth rings'; some deposits around hot springs develop concentric and rounded (botryoidal) structures reminiscent of pisolitic limestones		
Occurrence	found in limestone areas, in		

Evaporites

Evaporites are chemical sediments formed by the precipitation of dissolved salts through the evaporation of water. Although gypsum and halite are the most common, evaporite deposits often contain other minerals in lesser amounts, including the potassium and magnesium salts sylvite, carnallite, polyhalite, kainite and kieserite. Evaporites are of great economic importance. They often form the cap rock in many oilfields. Their low density enables them to rise through other rocks – a process called *diapirism* – and form structural traps for oil and natural gas.

Daisy bed

Halite and polyhalite in clay

dolomitic clay matrix

Rock salt

	EVAPORITES		
Colour	colourless or white; variously coloured by impurities, often browns		partings of shale; gypsum often interbedded with sandstone, mudstone or limestone
Mineralogy	rock salt is essentially halite, with impurities of associated salts (carbonates and sulphates), clay minerals and iron oxides; rock gypsum is often associated with anhydrite, calcite, dolomite, clay minerals and iron oxides	**Occurrence**	formed by the evaporation of salt-rich waters in lagoons, seas and lakes; gypsum may form by the action of water on anhydrite deposits
Texture	massive, saccharoidal (sugary) or coarsely crystalline; gypsum may be fibrous, earthy or crumbly	**Examples**	gypsum is common in the USA, as in the Carboniferous rocks of Utah, Permian rocks of New Mexico and Texas, and Cretaceous rocks of Florida; alabaster at Volterra (Italy), Iran and Pakistan; rock salt in NE Yorkshire (England), Siberia (USSR), NW Europe and Devonian Prairie Formation of Canada
Structure	may show bedding often strongly distorted; fossils rare; rock salt often in thick structureless beds with		

Ironstones

Ironstones are a group of iron-rich sedimentary rocks. They are potential iron ores and have a characteristic rust-coloured appearance on weathering. Their origins and the nature of the iron-containing minerals present vary so widely that some people call them 'iron formations' rather than ironstones. Precambrian banded iron formations occur in old cratonic (shield) areas. They usually form thick sequences of iron minerals interbedded with cherts. Such ironstones are of great economic importance. Deposits from the Cambrian period onwards are usually thin and oolitic. The only iron deposits forming today are the bog iron ores of mid- to high-latitude lakes and swamps. Ironstones often contain fossils.

Ironstone

Crudely bedded ironstone

fossils

Fossiliferous ironstone

Ironstone

fossil mould

	IRONSTONES	
Colour	brown, red, green or yellow	
Mineralogy	iron minerals present to give at least 15 per cent iron in the rock are commonly limonite, goethite, hematite, magnetite, pyrite, siderite, chamosite and glauconite; often cemented by calcite or dolomite	
Texture	variable grain size and variable texture; sometimes oolitic	
Structure	may be banded otherwise sedimentary structures common; fossils may be present	
Occurrence	often interbedded with cherts, limestones and sandstones; ironstones	themselves may also be classified as other sedimentary rocks (e.g. sandstones, limestones, shales)
Examples		large Precambrian iron-formations are in the Lake Superior region (North America) and the Hamersley Group of NW Australia; later ironstones are the Clinton Ironstone, Central Appalachian Basin (USA) the Rhiwbina Iron Ore (S Wales) and the Northampton, Cleveland and Frodingham Ironstones (England); modern freshwater bog ores are in Sweden and Finland

Cherts and Flints

Chert and flint are the traditional names for sedimentary chalcedony. However today, the term chert is preferred, while flint is used for a type of nodular chert occurring in chalk deposits. Cherts in the form of nodules occur most often in limestones and are often concentrated along one bedding plane. The silica in chalks comes from the remains of sponges, while, in deep-water limestones, it comes from radiolaria and diatoms (siliceous planktonic micro-organisms). Massive bedded cherts are formed from the skeletons of radiolaria and diatoms that are often deposited in deep water. The hardness of flint and its conchoidal fracture result in a sharp cutting edge, a property exploited by Stone Age people for making tools and weapons. For this reason care should be taken when handling cherts.

conchoidal fracture

Flint nodule

Banded chert

Flint tools

	CHERTS AND FLINTS	
Colour	blue-grey to almost black when nodular, weathering to a white powdery crust (patina); massive bedded cherts may be brown, green or black	
Mineralogy	essentially silica as chalcedony	
Texture	very fine-grained with smooth, conchoidal fracture	
Structure	flint and chert form rounded nodules of varying forms; chert also forms massive thinly bedded deposits	
Occurrence	nodules of flint and chert are often concentrated along the bedding planes of limestones and chalks; bedded radiolarian cherts form in lakes and marine areas with little other sedimentation	
Examples	flint is found throughout the Upper Cretaceous Chalk of W Europe, especially SE England; radiolarian cherts are found in Wales (Millstone Grit series), Devon (England), Rhine Valley (Germany) and the Franciscan cherts of the Coastal Range of California and Oregon (USA); modern deposits of radiolarian ooze are found in the depths of the Indian and Pacific Oceans	

Phosphatic Rocks

Phosphate-rich rocks, or phosphorites, form in seas where there is little sedimentation and where cold, nutrient-rich water wells up to the surface. The upwelling causes a high growth of phytoplankton and other surface organisms which can poison fish, causing mass mortalities. Because all organisms contain phosphates, especially in their bones, their remains produce phosphate-rich sediments. Smaller-scale phosphorites, formed from the skeletons of vertebrates, are called *bone beds*. The excrement of sea birds (*guano*) can produce economically useful deposits for the fertilizer and chemical industries. They are insignificant geologically.

Polished slice of phosphorite

Bone bed

bone fragments

Phosphorite

PHOSPHATIC ROCKS	
Colour	white, yellow, brown, black
Mineralogy	complex phosphates of calcium, aluminium and iron; detrital sedimentary material usually present
Texture	fine- to coarse-grained when bedded; compact, earthy, granular, sometimes oolitic; guano is earthy and crumbles easily
Structure	bedded phosphate rocks mostly nodular with organic remains often replaced by phosphates; guano usually bedded
Occurrence	mainly associated with marine sediments, especially greensands, limestones and shales; guano, being the accumulated excrement of sea-birds, is associated with oceanic islands
Examples	phosphorites are found in Tennessee and California, and the Permian Phosphoria Formation of Idaho (USA); Ludlow Bone Bed and Rhaetic Bone Beds (SW England), Tertiary rocks of Algeria, Iraq, Morocco, Tunisia, Turkey and Western Sahara

Carbonaceous Sediments

Carbonaceous sediments include peat and coal. Most coals are *humic* (formed from degraded wood), and some are *sapropelic* (formed from plant debris, spores and algae). Coals form a series with increasing carbon content, caused by increasing pressure and temperature on burial. The coals with the highest proportion of carbon are usually the oldest. *Lignite* or soft brown coals have a porous structure, resembling dried peat. Hard brown coals and *bituminous coals*, including household and coking coals, have an 85 to 90 per cent carbon content and contain volatiles, including hydrogen. *Steam coal* is hard and brittle. Shiny black *anthracite* is almost pure carbon, with a low content of volatile material.

Peat

Anthracite

Bituminous coal

Lignite

	CARBONACEOUS SEDIMENTS	
Colour	light, brownish peat through to black coals	
Mineralogy	peat is mainly vegetable remains with various detrital materials; anthracite is almost pure carbon; coals may contain pyrite or other minerals	
Texture	peat is felt-like and soft; lignite is like dried, woody peat; bituminous coals are hard and bright breaking into rectangular lumps; anthracite is shiny with conchoidal fracture	
Structure	peat has little structure; bituminous hard coals usually have a distinctive	bedding and prominent joint surfaces called *cleats*; fossil plant material may be clearly visible on bedding planes
Occurrence		peat occurs in marshes and lakes in temperate and subarctic climates; most coals, as strata formed by the burial and alteration of woody material often alternating with sandstone and clay
Examples		peat bogs are common in Ireland, Scotland, Poland and Canada; Carboniferous rocks of Europe and North America contain harder, older coals; soft brown coals occur in newer rocks in France and Germany

Index

Index

KINGFISHER NATURAL HISTORY

If you find this book useful, you may be interested in the other
natural history titles published by Kingfisher Books:

Field Guides
Birds of Britain & Europe
Birds of Britain & Ireland
Mammals of Britain & Europe
Mushrooms & Toadstools of Britain & Europe
Plant Life of Britain & Europe
Trees of Britain & Europe
Wild Flowers of Britain & Europe
Wildlife of Britain & Europe

Complete Guides
The Complete Birdwatcher's Guide
*The Complete Guide to the Wildlife
of Britain & Europe*

General
The Natural History of Britain & Europe

Acknowledgements

The publishers wish to thank the following for kindly supplying
photographs for this book: David Baker; Ron Boardman, Life Science
Images; Peter Green, Imitor; Mike Grey; Natural History Museum,
London; ZEFA.

The publishers wish to thank the following for providing specimens for
photography: Professor M. Audley-Charles and Wendy Kirk of the
University College of London; Daphne Kirk; Richard Taylor.

Colour photographs: Peter Green and Mike Grey